THE STAR OF
BETHLEHEM

THE STAR OF
BETHLEHEM

PATRICK MOORE

CANOPUS PUBLISHING LIMITED

© Canopus Publishing Limited 2001

First published in 2001 by
Canopus Publishing Limited
Registered office: 48 Cranwells Park, Bath BA1 2YE, UK
Reprinted 2005

The moral right of the author has been asserted

A catalogue record for this book is available from the British Library

ISBN 0 9537868 2 X

Subedited by Pam Spence
Proofread by Sarah Tremlett
Artwork by Julian Baum
Designed and typeset by Kevin Lowry
Printed and bound in Great Britain by Cromwell Press, Trowbridge

Acknowledgements

My thanks are due to David Hughes and to Mark Kidger, who have written the definitive books about the Star of Bethlehem, and who have given me all possible help even though I have come to conclusions different from theirs. Allan Chapman has read through my manuscript and made some invaluable suggestions. Christopher Doherty has provided me with some splendid photographs. And my particular thanks go to Robin Rees of Canopus Publishing Limited, without whose encouragement this book would not have been written.

Patrick Moore
Selsey, 29 June 2001

CONTENTS

CHAPTER 1

FICTION OR FACT?

Who has not heard of the 'star in the east'? It is one of the most famous stories in the Bible, and tells us how the wise men came to Bethlehem to seek out the infant Jesus; they were guided by a brilliant star, which "went before them" and stopped over the place where the child lay. Though all this happened two thousand years ago, the fascination of the Star of Bethlehem is as great as ever. But is the story true – and if so, what exactly was the 'star'?

Nobody has yet been able to give an answer to either of these questions, and I do not pretend to be able to do so; in any case I am an astronomer, not a Biblical scholar. Yet though I cannot tell you what the star was, I hope I can give you some ideas about what it was not. We will look at the various theories, of which there are many, and see what we can make of them. First, we must check upon our sources of information.

I say 'sources', but in fact there is only one really useful source: the Gospel according to St Matthew, chapter 2, verses 1 to 12, and verse 16. The quotes below come from the authorised King James version of the Bible. The New Revised Standard version, given in the Appendix, says the same thing in slightly less archaic language.

"Now when Jesus was born in Bethlehem of Judaea in the days of Herod the king, behold, there came wise men from the east to Jerusalem. Saying, Where is he that is born King of the Jews? for we have seen his star in the east, and are come to worship him.

"When Herod the king had heard *these things*, he was troubled, and all Jerusalem with him. And when he had gathered all the chief priests and scribes of the people together, he demanded of them where Christ should be born.

"And they said unto him, In Bethlehem of Judaea; for thus it is written by the prophet, And thou Bethlehem, in the land of Judah, art not the least among the princes of Judah: for out of thee shall come a Governor, that shall rule my people Israel.

"Then Herod, when he had privily called the wise men, inquired of them diligently what time the star appeared. And he sent them to Bethlehem, and said, Go and search diligently for the young child; and when ye have found *him*, bring me word again, that I may come and worship him also.

"When they had heard the king, they departed; and, lo, the star, which they saw in the east, went before them, till it came and stood over where the young child was. When they saw the star, they rejoiced with exceeding great joy.

"And when they were come into the house, they saw the young child with Mary his mother, and fell down, and worshipped him: and when they had opened their treasures, they presented unto him gifts; gold, and frankincense, and myrrh."

(Have you any idea what frankincense and myrrh are? Well, frankincense is an aromatic gum resin obtained from trees, chiefly East African, of genus Boswellia and burnt as incense. Myrrh is a gum resin, obtained from various species, especially *Commiphora molmol*, used in perfumes and incense, and in medicine as astringent and antiseptic mouthwash. I thought you'd like to know!)

St Matthew chapter 2, verses 12 and 16 continue:

"And being warned of God in a dream that they should not return to Herod, they departed into their own country another way.

"Then Herod, when he saw that he was mocked of the wise men, was exceeding wroth, and sent forth, and slew all the children that were in Bethlehem, and in all the coasts thereof, from two years old and under, according to the time which he had diligently inquired of the wise men."

That is all. St Matthew says no more, and the other Gospels do not mention the star at all, though insofar as the Nativity is concerned, Luke is much more informative than Matthew.

From the very beginning, therefore, we have to admit that our information is painfully scanty. But one thing is very clear; the wise men were wise enough not to go back to

Herod who was definitely not a nice man, and who had the pleasant little habit of executing anyone who crossed his path. His methods included burning alive, drowning and strangulation, and among those disposed of were several of his children – including three of his sons, one of whom was the eldest, Antipater. (Augustus, Emperor of Rome, is believed to have said that he would rather be Herod's pig than Herod's son, which under the circumstances was fair comment.)

Herod was not even a Jew; he was an Idumaenean, and came from the Land of Edom, a desert region to the south of Judea. He had been made king by the Romans, and ruled as an absolute tyrant from 37 BC to 4 BC. The Edomites claimed a common descent from the Jews, and Herod did adopt Jewish customs, but, not surprisingly, he was not beloved by his subjects, and the massacre of the children in Bethlehem was quite in keeping with his character.

St Matthew's account is the only one to be written reasonably close to the time of the Nativity, though even this came decades later, and we are not absolutely sure about the authorship. Later references are clearly second-hand, and only two seem to be worth mentioning here.

One is due to Ignatius, the second Bishop of Antioch in Syria. Early in the second century – possibly around AD 107 – he was arrested by the Roman authorities and condemned to death, so that he was transported to Rome and was, as convention dictated, eaten by lions. In his epistle to the Ephesians, he says that at the time of the Nativity "a star shone forth in heaven above all the other stars, the light of which was inexpressible, while its novelty struck men with astonishment. And all the rest of the stars, with the Sun and Moon, formed a chorus to this star, and its light was exceedingly great above them all."

There is also the Protoevangelium of James, one of the infancy gospels left out of the Bible when the New Testament was put together. In this version, Herod asked the wise men what they had seen, and they replied: "We saw how an indescribably greater star shone among these stars and dimmed them, so that they no longer shone, and so we knew that a king was born for Israel. And we have come to worship him." The rest of the account is very much the same as that in the King James, but it does not seem that the book can have been written before about AD 150, and the author may not have been Jewish, because he does not give the impression of knowing a great deal about Jewish customs or Palestinian geography. By AD 150, Christianity was well spread into Greek and Latin regions.

Both Ignatius and James say that the star was blindingly brilliant, but Matthew gives no suggestion of this, as he would surely have done if the other stars were 'dimmed'. All in all, it is best to put our trust in Matthew. Although there appears to be just the one fairly contemporary source, anthropologists are aware how accurate and persistent oral traditions were in cultures where the written word was not in daily use. I agree that it is infuriatingly vague, but the chances of any new information being found after an interval of two thousand years seem to be effectively nil, so we must make the best use of what little we have.

There are several possibilities:

1 The whole story is a myth, in which case we can have no idea of its origin.

2 The star was supernatural.

3 The story was invented by Matthew to add colour to his account of the Nativity – or was added later by another author.

4   The star was a genuine astronomical phenomenon.

5   The star was a UFO – or, if you like, a flying saucer –
        dispatched to Earth by some alien civilization far
        away in space.

First it seems necessary to say something about the wise
men. The first Magi may have been Zoroastrians, a cult
founded around 1000 BC; Zoroaster was a monotheist, a
person who believed in only one God and who believed that
there would come a king who would raise the dead and
change the world into a realm of security and peace
(something which, alas, has not yet happened).

The Magi were well respected, and were very influential.
Of course they were astrologers as well as stargazers, and this
is a very important point, because to them the appearance of
the star – assuming that it appeared at all – was primarily of
astrological importance. We are not at all sure where the wise
men came from before they arrived in Jerusalem, but it may
well have been Persia.

The tradition of 'three kings of Orient' is equally vague.
There may have been more than three, and it is not likely
that they were 'kings' in the accepted sense. However, it is
probable that they had a good knowledge of the sky, and
would not have been deceived by anything as commonplace
as a planet. Scientific astronomy was well established by this
time, mainly of course by the Greeks, and good star
catalogues had been drawn up, as we know from the classic
encyclopedia written by Ptolemy of Alexandria around AD
150. Whether the wise men were familiar with the Greek
work is uncertain, but there seems no reason why not.

Incidentally, it seems strange that Herod did not send a
guard to Bethlehem with the wise men; after all, Bethlehem
is less than two hours walk from Jerusalem, and Herod had

taken the trouble to meet the Magi in secret. Possibly it simply did not occur to him that they would beat a prudent retreat, but again we will never know.

What follows must be largely coloured by my own views, and I am well aware that many people – perhaps most – will disagree with them, but at least they may form a basis for discussion. So let us begin with the first suggestion: that the whole story is completely without foundation.

I do not feel we can go very far down this road, because the implication is that the entire New Testament is baseless. This idea would not appeal to historians, either Christian or pagan, or even to archaeologists. No doubt parts of the Bible have been grossly distorted with respect to the actual events, but it is very hard to believe that they can be discounted altogether. So let us turn to the next possibility: that the star was purely supernatural.

CHAPTER 2

MIRACULOUS STAR

Mysticism is an integral part of every religion. It is certainly the case with Christianity, and anything else would be surprising; this applies even today, when people are in general much more sceptical than they used to be. Therefore there is bound to be a mystical association with the birth of Christ, and what could be more suitable than a celestial portent?

St Matthew's was probably the second Gospel composed after St Mark's. It was written predominantly for a Jewish audience, to convert Jews to Christianity by showing Christ as the fulfilment of the prophecy of a Messiah. Very little is known about Matthew, but even if the Gospel was not written by one man it would have been written by followers of Matthew, men in the same style of Christian experience. It is possible that the story about the star was added after the original text had been written, but most scholars regard deliberate embellishment as rather improbable, if only because there seems no need for it.

Neither is there any obvious connection with mythology; after all, myths are essentially pagan, and would not be expected to have any real link with the Nativity, even though many of the Greek gods were born in rather curious ways. Claiming that the star was supernatural is different. This is what many people have believed, and still do.

'Creation theory' is still rampant, particularly in some parts of the United States. American Creationism is a twentieth-century product of an extreme Protestant culture, and the Creationists claim that everything in the Bible is to be taken literally; they have no time for Darwinism, and they maintain that the world was created at precisely 10 o'clock in the morning of 26 October 4004 BC. (I have never decided whether they made due allowance for Summer Time.) Such was the view of the seventeenth-century Bishop Ussher of Armagh, who arrived at this date by adding up the ages of the patriarchs and making other equally irrelevant calculations.

The idea that men might have the same ancestors as monkeys was, to these folk, not only sacrilegious but also illogical; fossils, they maintained, could not be more than a few centuries old. In some modern American schools it is laid down that Creationism and Darwinism must be given equal weight in all lessons. In the Creationist view, the star was a real phenomenon, but a supernatural one; it was put into the sky specifically to mark the birth of Christ. It could even have been a natural event, such as a supernova, sent by God to herald Christ's birth.

If this is true, then we have gone beyond science. There is nothing more to be added, certainly from an astronomical point of view, so there is no point in looking back at the astronomical records. A celestial portent introduced especially for the wise men would not be seen by anyone else, and could be made to move in a way which was suited to

Bishop Ussher of Armagh. Reproduced by kind permission of the
Governors and Guardians of Armagh Public Library.

the occasion. One might expect similar portents to be introduced for other key figures in religion – Buddha, for example – but this does not appear to be so, and of course Christian scholars will always maintain that Christianity is a special case. Perhaps it may be as well to leave it at that, and let people decide for themselves. In this book I am concerned with science, and miracles are outside my field.

Associated with this, admittedly rather loosely, is the idea that the star might have been due to a flying saucer (or, in more dignified terms, a UFO). Here there really is a link with science, because most scientists – not all – believe that life is widespread in the universe, and that we humans are most certainly not unique.

Up to now we have no hard and fast proof that life flourishes anywhere else, but it seems both illogical and conceited to think that we are exceptional. The Earth is an ordinary planet, moving round an ordinary star. Our Galaxy contains around 100 thousand million stars, many of them strikingly similar to the Sun, and there is absolutely no reason to doubt that they are attended by planets very like the Earth.

We have already proved that there are planets orbiting other stars far away in space, and though it is true that the planets so far detected are gas giants, not unlike our Jupiter and totally unsuited to intelligent life, it is surely only a matter of time before other 'Earths' are found. This means that there are many millions of worlds in our Galaxy alone where life could exist.

Yet can we be confident that life will appear wherever conditions are suited to it, and will evolve as far as local circumstances will allow? We may have a better idea in the near future, because if all goes well we may identify very primitive, single-celled living things on Mars.

Mars is a world much smaller than the Earth, moving round the Sun at a greater distance (on average 141,500,000

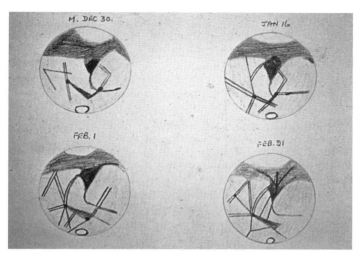

The canals of Mars, as drawn by Percival Lowell in 1897.

miles (230,000,000 kilometres), as against 93,000,000 miles (150,000,000 kilometres) for the Earth). It has a very thin atmosphere, made up of the unbreathable gas carbon dioxide, and it is bitterly cold. Less than a century ago it was widely believed that there were Martians who had built an elaborate canal system to carry water from the icy poles through to the centres of population; astronomers such as Percival Lowell, in America, drew streaks crossing the Martian deserts which they regarded as artificial waterways.

In fact the canals do not exist; they were tricks of the eye. If there is life on Mars it must be very lowly, but we cannot rule it out. Plans are being made to send unmanned spacecraft there, collect samples and bring them back for analysis. If they do contain any living organisms, it will indicate that life will appear wherever it can. At present I have an open mind, but even if Mars proves to be sterile, we still cannot dismiss the idea of life elsewhere. To repeat an old cliché: 'absence of proof is not proof of absence'.

It is reasonable to assume that some other races, elsewhere in the Galaxy, are far in advance of ourselves. They may well have mastered the art of interstellar travel, in which case they could be capable of sending spacecraft to the Earth. 'Was Christ an astronaut?' has been the theme of several widely-read books, and the idea that the Star of Bethlehem was an interstellar probe, sent here either fortuitously or on purpose, has been mooted time and time again. Again there is little point in speculating further, but most people will share my scepticism.

(I would very much like to meet a traveller from 'outer space', but I doubt whether I will ever have that privilege. I have often been asked how I would react if a flying saucer landed in my garden and a little green man emerged, saying 'Take me to your leader'. I know exactly what my response would be. 'Good afternoon. Tea or coffee? Then please come with me to the nearest television studio!')

Despite the idea of a plurality of worlds having been actively discussed for at least 350 years, if we did manage to make contact with ETI, or Extra-Terrestrial Intelligence, our whole philosophy would be changed beyond recognition; and how the churches would manage to cope with it I know not. It may happen. Radio waves travel at the same speed as light: 186,000 miles per second (300,000 kilometres per second), and there are several solar-type stars which are well within what we call radio range. Serious efforts at contact are now being made, and though the chances of success may be slight, they are certainly not nil. If we do find other civilizations as advanced as we are or even more so, will they have their own Christs, their own Buddhas and their own signs in the sky? One day, perhaps, we will find out. But for the moment, let me return to my main theme.

CHAPTER 3

A QUESTION OF TIME

One problem facing us when we begin a scientific investigation of the Star of Bethlehem is that we are decidedly unsure about our dates. The one thing about which we can be absolutely certain is that Christ was not born on 25 December AD 1. He cannot have been born in the year 0, because there was no year 0; the zero had not then been invented – it came along much later – and Roman numbers were used. They were, to put it mildly, inconvenient. If you doubt me, try multiplying MCMXVI by LXXXVIII.

The result is that the year 1 BC was followed immediately by AD 1, and this has caused confusion even in our own time, because it was widely believed that the new millennium must begin on 1 January 2000. Predictably governments fell into this trap, and declared a public holiday on the last day of 1999. The new millennium started on 1 January 2001, but in any case the entire system is meaningless, quite apart from the fact that it relates to the Christian creed only.

Our AD dates are reckoned according to the calculations of a Scythian monk, Dionysius Exiguus, who died in AD 556. He gave the date of Christ's birth as 754 years later than the founding of Rome, and this has become so firmly established that the system will never be altered now, even though it is quite definitely wrong; Christ was born several years earlier than Dionysius believed. Moreover, 25 December was not celebrated as Christmas Day until the fourth century AD – by which time the real date had been forgotten, so that our Christmas is wrong too.

(*En passant*, the name 'Dionysius Exiguus' really means 'Dennis the Little' in Greek. This does not indicate that he was short in stature. He seems to have been a very modest man, and took the name Exiguus, 'little one', to distinguish him from an earlier Dionysius, whom he regarded as far more eminent.)

We must look rather more closely at the calendar, because if we are to link up with any astronomical phenomena it is essential to decide upon the date of the Nativity. Dionysius did his best, but he made two serious mistakes. He omitted the year 0, as we have noted, but he also left out four vital years because his method was to count backwards through the reigns of the Roman Emperors, and he forgot that Augustus, Julius Caesar's adopted son, ruled for four years under his original name of Octavian. Even if Dionysius were right in all other respects, this means that Christ was actually born in the year we call 5 BC. It also means that technically our own millennium began in 1997, though none of the Christian churches seemed to take any notice – as a point of faith, the date is irrelevant; it is the Incarnation as an event which matters.

One important clue is that King Herod died in 4 BC. All the historical evidence points that way, and there seems no real doubt about it. Consequently, since Christ was born before Herod's death, the Nativity must have been in or earlier than 4 BC.

The Bible says, quite clearly, that Herod died soon after an eclipse of the Moon, but before the following Passover, which gives a span of 29 days. The only lunar eclipses visible from Jerusalem around this time were those of 23 March 5

Lunar eclipse; photographed by Henry Brinton, 1967

BC, 15 September 5 BC, and 13 March 4 BC. The last of these is the only eclipse to have occurred less than a month before Passover, so Herod must have died in late March or early April in 4 BC, by which time Christ had been born. It is true that the March eclipse was only partial, with no more than 35 per cent of the Moon shadowed, but it seems to be the only candidate. The next eclipses – on 17 July 2 BC and 9 January 1 BC – are too late.

Also, the Roman historian Flavius Josephus states that Herod executed two rabbis at the time of the eclipse, because he accused them of inciting young men to tear down the statue of an eagle that Herod had caused to be set up on the gate to the temple in Jerusalem. Josephus adds that Herod died soon afterwards, and this agrees well with the eclipse of 4 BC.

We know that Herod knew about Christ's birth, which is why he ordered all the young boys in Bethlehem to be slaughtered. And Herod died not long afterwards, doubtless regretted by none. If the interval between the slaughter and Herod's death were as much as one year, and Christ was then two years old, the date of the Nativity can be put back to 7 BC, but this must be the very limit acceptable, and 5 BC is much more likely.

Not everybody agrees. The British astronomer and historian David Hughes, who has probably given as much attention to the problem as any living scholar, prefers 7 BC. If we take this as being the earliest possible date, and 4 BC the latest, we have a span of only three years, and this does at least help us in trying to pin down any relevant celestial phenomena. Anything before 7 BC or after 4 BC can definitely be ruled out, and this narrows our search a great deal.

As for 25 December – well, the first suggestion that this was the date of the Nativity was given in a Roman city calendar for the year AD 354, and since this is so long after the event it can hardly be more than a guess, though as there were "shepherds abiding in the field" (St Luke, chapter 2 verse 8), spring seems a likely season. However there is no chance of moving our Christmas Day, even if we wanted to do so, and what would be the point? Any other day selected would be equally unreliable.

At this stage it may be worth noting that Jesus and his

family were not ordinary Galilean settlers; they were recent immigrants. Reports of a census taken in 6 BC tell us that they were forced to move south from Nazareth to Bethlehem to register at Joseph's home, near Jerusalem. (See 'The Star of Bethlehem', by the Rev. Professor William Friend, in *Year-book of Astronomy* 1996, Macmillan, London.) In Nazareth the family had been influential, and owned land as far afield as Capernaum on the Lake of Gennasaret. Both Christ's parents were able to trace their ancestry back to the Royal House of David, and, contrary to popular belief, the baby was born in a house, not a stable. All this is very different from the scene usually shown on Christmas cards, and may be regarded as unromantic, but it seems to be fairly definite.

For our present purpose, I propose to adopt the majority view that Christ was born at some time during the year 5 BC. This may be slightly too early or slightly too late, but from the purely astronomical point of view it does not make a great deal of difference. If we had to deal with a much greater window of uncertainty, it would be virtually impossible to make any serious suggestions about the real nature of the Star of Bethlehem.

CHAPTER 4

THE FAMILIAR SKY

The night sky is always changing, but only within certain limits. The constellation patterns do not alter obviously over immensely long periods, and this means that they were, to all intents and purposes, the same in the time of Christ as they are now. The wise men would have seen the Great Bear, the Little Bear, Orion, the Pleiades and the rest just as we do today. It is only our near neighbours – the members of the Solar System – which wander around, and even they keep to certain well-defined regions of the sky.

The reason for this is that the stars are so far away. In astronomy we have to deal with distances so vast that ordinary units of measurement, such as the mile and the kilometre, are hopelessly inconvenient, just as it would be clumsy to give the distance between, say, London and Manchester in inches. (In case you are interested, the answer would be around 11,594,880.) The stars are suns, many of them far larger, hotter and more luminous than ours, and the size of the observable universe is beyond our comprehension.

Light does not travel instantaneously; it speeds along at a rate of 186,000 miles per second (300,000 kilometres per second). In a year, therefore, it covers almost 6 million million miles, and this is what we term a light-year (9.5 million million kilometres). The nearest star beyond the Sun, a faint red dwarf known as Proxima Centauri, is over 4 light-years away; the Pole Star is 680 light-years from us, Rigel in Orion about 900 light-years, and so on.

Look at the Pole Star, and you will see it as it used to be 680 years ago, in the time of the Crusades. If some malevolent giant suddenly snatched the Pole Star out of the sky, it would be AD 2681 before we could realize that anything untoward had happened. Once we look beyond our immediate neighbourhood, our view of the universe is bound to be very out of date. Even the Sun is seen as it used to be 8.6 minutes ago.

Consider a sparrow flying around at treetop height, and a jet aircraft silhouetted against the clouds. The sparrow moves quickly while the jet seems to crawl, but in reality the jet is moving much the faster of the two. The rule is: 'the further, the slower', and the stars are so remote that their individual or proper motions are tiny. Eventually, of course, the shifts will become noticeable.

Using modern-type instruments we can measure the proper motions, and we know how the stars are moving. In the famous pattern in the Great Bear, known commonly as the Plough or (in America) as the Big Dipper, two of the stars are moving in a direction opposite to the other five, so that in, say, 50,000 years from now, the pattern will have become distorted.

The constellation patterns are quite arbitrary, because the stars are at very different distances from us, and we are dealing with nothing more significant than line of sight

The Great Bear, showing the way to the Pole Star.

effects. In Orion (see page 88), the two leading stars are the orange-red Betelgeux and the bluish-white Rigel. Betelgeux is 310 light-years away (according to the *Cambridge catalogue*), while Rigel lies about 900 light-years from us, so that Rigel is a great deal further away from Betelgeux than we are.

The last great astronomer of ancient times was Ptolemy of Alexandria, who lived from around AD 120 to 180. In his book, which has come down to us via its Arab translation and is known as the *Almagest*, he listed 48 constellations, all of which are still used in our present-day maps, though admittedly with altered boundaries.

Ptolemy's star catalogue was based on that of an earlier Greek astronomer, Hipparchus, who flourished about 140 BC, well before the time of Christ; but even Hipparchus did not draw up the original constellation patterns, and we are not at all sure who did. It may have been the stargazers of the Minoan civilization in Crete, which some authorities (not all) believe to have been destroyed around 1500 BC by the violent eruption of the Santorini volcano, some way off the Cretan coast.

In any case, many of our constellations have names based on Greek mythology: Orion, Cepheus, Cassiopeia, Andromeda and so on – but all this is purely arbitrary. The other ancient civilizations, those of China and Egypt, used different patterns; for example the Egyptians had a cat and a hipopotamus. If we had followed one of the other systems, our maps would look very different from those which we actually use, though the stars themselves would be exactly the same.

The planets look like stars, but at an early stage in Greek science it was realized that they are completely different in nature, since they move slowly around from one constellation to another. However, their range is limited, and for example you will never see a planet anywhere near the Great Bear or Cassiopeia. They keep strictly to a band round the sky known as the Zodiac. The reason, as we now know, is that their orbits round the Sun are more or less in the same plane, so that if you draw a plan of the Solar System on a piece of flat paper you are not very far wrong.

Relative to the orbit of the Earth, the inclinations of the orbits of the other planets are 7 degrees for Mercury and less than 4 degrees for all the rest (apart from Pluto, which was not discovered until 1930, and which is too faint to be seen except through a telescope of reasonable size).

Of course the ancients knew nothing about the real nature of the planets, and most of the old astronomers believed the Earth to lie at rest in the exact centre of the universe, but they did make very accurate measurements of planetary movements.

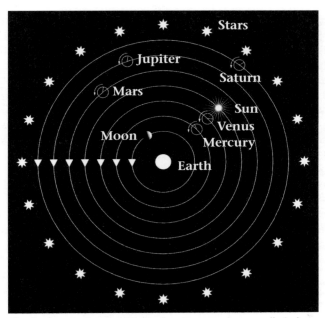

The Ptolemaic System. Each planet moves in a small circle, or epicycle, the centre of which, the deferent, itself moves round the Earth in a perfect circle.

Indeed, their observations were surprisingly precise in view of the fact that they had to rely upon the naked eye alone; telescopes did not come upon the scene for over fourteen centuries after Ptolemy's death.

In the *Almagest*, Ptolemy gives a detailed description of the universe as he believed it to be. The Earth was central and motionless, and round it moved the Moon, Sun, planets and the realm of the fixed stars. The stars were supposed to be attached to a crystal sphere, so that they would all be at the same distance from us.

I must pause here to say something about astrology, which claims to link the movements of the planets with human character and destiny. All the old astronomers were also astrologers, and particular attention was paid to the planetary motions. Indeed, astrology was widely regarded as being the more important of the two studies.

Scorpius is often, though incorrectly, called Scorpio. A thirteenth constellation, Ophiuchus (the Serpent-bearer) intrudes into the Zodiac between Scorpius and Sagittarius, so that planets can, and do, pass through it. Astrologers have never been able to make up their minds about Ophiuchus, and do their best to pretend that it does not exist.

Note that the Zodiacal constellations are very unequal in size and brilliance. Thus Leo, Gemini and Scorpius are very prominent, while Cancer and Pisces are dull and formless. It was Sir John Herschel, a famous nineteenth-century astronomer, who commented that the constellation patterns seemed to have been worked out so as to cause as much confusion and inconvenience as possible, but occasional attempts to redraw the sky maps have met with no support.

According to astrologers, the most important clue to the destiny of a human being is given by the positions of the planets at the time of birth. It does not require much

The Zodiac is divided into twelve constellations:	
Aries	the Ram
Taurus	the Bull
Gemini	the Twins
Cancer	the Crab
Leo	the Lion
Virgo	the Virgin
Libra	the Scales
Scorpius	the Scorpion
Sagittarius	the Archer
Capricornus	the Sea-goat
Aquarius	the Water-bearer
Pisces	the Fishes.

intelligence to see the absurdity of this, because the planets are much closer than the stars, and are simply in the foreground; to say that a planet is 'in' a constellation is the same as saying that a sparrow flying around at treetop height against a cloud background, is 'in' the cloud. Moreover, the stars are at very different distances from us, so that the constellation patterns are mere line of sight effects, and

The Zodiac: the constellations through which the planets appear to move as seen from Earth.

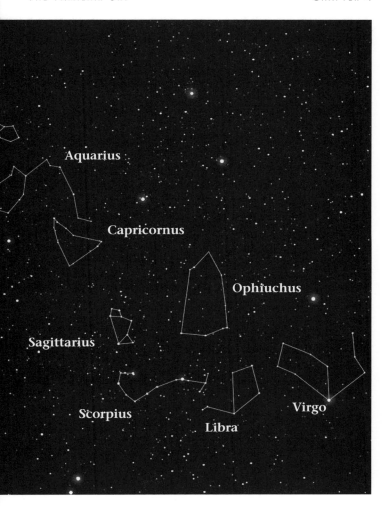

Aquarius

Capricornus

Ophiuchus

Sagittarius

Scorpius

Libra

Virgo

mean nothing at all. Yet astrology remains popular, and there are even a few professional astrologers who genuinely believe in it. On the whole it is harmless enough, provided that it is kept to fairground tents and seaside piers, but right up to mediaeval times it was still regarded as a true science.

All this is not really a digression, because it shows that the wise men must have had a good working knowledge of the sky, and in particular how the planets moved. When we start to look for astronomical phenomena which could be linked with the Star of Bethlehem, we must always remember that the Magi were not mere ignorant star-watchers.

Of the five planets known to them, two – Venus and Jupiter – are always much brighter than any star. Mars can also be brilliant enough to outshine the stars, though its distance from us varies and when at its faintest there is nothing to mark it out apart from the strong red colour which led to its being named in honour of the God of War. Saturn is bright enough to be conspicuous, and only Mercury tends to be elusive, though it can on occasion be reasonably prominent. So can any of these planets be identified with the Star of Bethlehem?

Venus has always been regarded as a favourite candidate, because it is the brightest object in the entire sky apart from the Sun and the Moon. At its best it can cast perceptible shadows, and looks like a small lamp in the sky. It is closer to the Sun than we are, with a mean distance of 67,000,000 miles (108,000,000 kilometres) as against 93,000,000 miles (150,000,000 kilometres) for the Earth, and it has an orbital period or 'year' of nearly 225 Earth-days. Its own 'day' is remarkably long, at 243 Earth-days; moreover Venus spins in an east to west direction, instead of west to east as with the Earth and Mars. The illustration shows the two orbits, and it is obvious that as seen from Earth, the Sun and Venus must always be in the same part of the sky. This

Mercury and Venus, the two planets nearest the Sun, always appear to be in the same part of the sky as the Sun as seen from Earth, the planet in the foreground.

means that Venus is visible in the west after sunset or in the east before dawn, but can never remain above the horizon all through the hours of darkness.

So far as appearance is concerned, Venus would seem to be a suitable candidate, but it would have been well known to the wise men, and there was nothing special about it during the period from 7 to 4 BC. If the wise men could be deceived by Venus, they could not be very wise!

Jupiter is not so brilliant as Venus, but it far outshines every star, and is on view for several months in each year. It is a long way away; its mean distance from the Sun is

483,000,000 miles (777,000,000 kilometres), and it has an orbital period of just under 12 years. It is prominent because of its size; Jupiter, with a diameter of nearly 90,000 miles (145,000 kilometres) is the giant of the Sun's family, and is more massive than all the other planets put together. It has a retinue of satellites, of which four (Io, Europa, Ganymede and Callisto) are of planetary size, and can be seen with any small telescope. They were first watched in detail by Galileo as long ago as 1610.

When the Sun, the Earth and Jupiter are more or less lined up, with the Earth in mid position, Jupiter and the Sun lie in opposite directions in the sky as viewed from Earth, and Jupiter reaches opposition, i.e. it is due south at midnight (assuming that you are observing from the northern hemisphere of the Earth) and is ideally placed for observation. Jupiter moves round the Sun more slowly than we do, and has further to go, so that when the Earth has made one complete circuit Jupiter has not moved nearly so far. The Earth takes about a month to 'catch it up', so to speak, and the result is that oppositions occur every 399 days or so. The wise men would have known all about this, and the fact that they believed Jupiter to move round the Earth rather than round the Sun made no difference.

Like Venus, therefore, Jupiter can be ruled out except under very special circumstances. We need waste no time on Saturn or Mercury, neither of which are brilliant enough to be candidates, and both of which were familiar objects. I think that we can also discount Mars; there were oppositions in 7 BC and 5 BC, but on neither occasion was the planet outstandingly bright.

If we reject the planets, what about the stars? The same objections are valid. Much the brightest of the stars is Sirius in Canis Major, the Great Dog, which can be found by following the line of the three stars making up Orion's Belt, but it, too, was very familiar. For part of the year it is too close to the Sun in the sky to be seen, because it is then above the horizon only during daylight. When it begins to emerge, it can be seen rising in the east before dawn, and this 'heliacal rising' was used by the Egyptians to regulate their calendar; it happens at the time of the annual inundation of the Nile, upon which their whole economy depended. To the Egyptians, Sirius was a very important star. They called it Sothis.

Heliacal rising. A reconstruction of how Sirius might have appeared rising in the east over the Nile in 5 BC.

As a candidate Sirius can be ruled out at once, but there is one other star which is particularly bright: Canopus, in the constellation of Carina, the Keel of the Ship. Canopus does not look as brilliant as Sirius, but appearances are deceptive. We now know that Sirius is one of our closest stellar neighbours, a mere 8.6 light-years away and 26 times as luminous as the Sun; Canopus is a cosmic searchlight, lying at a distance of well over 1000 light-years, and shining 200,000 times more powerfully than the Sun.

Why do I single out Canopus rather than Sirius? The reason is that it lies further south in the sky. It is not visible from anywhere in Europe, and the fact that it can be seen from Alexandria but not from Athens was one of the earliest proofs that the Earth is a globe rather than a flat plane. From Jerusalem it does rise… just. It peers briefly above the horizon, but never attains an altitude of more than 5 degrees, so that the wise men would not have been really familiar with it. All the same, it is most unlikely that Canopus can have been the Star of Bethlehem. It simply does not meet the necessary requirements.

What are these requirements? At this point it will be useful to list them, and assuming that we put our trust in St Matthew they seem to me to be as follows:

1   The star must have been unusual.

2   It must have been conspicuous.

3   It may have been seen only by the wise men.

4   It must have appeared during the period from 7 to 4 BC.

5   Either it cannot have lasted for long, or else it must

have appeared, vanished and then reappeared at a suitable moment.

6   It must have moved in a way quite unlike that of any normal star or planet.

Candidly, the object in the night sky which could fulfil all these requirements is a flying saucer – and this I absolutely refuse to believe. But at least we can try to find an object meeting enough of the requirements to be a serious candidate, and as a start we can dismiss all the stars, and all the planets under normal conditions, as failing requirements 1, 3, 5 and 6.

We must delve deeper.

CHAPTER 5

WANDERING STARS

We have already weeded out all the 'fixed stars' as possible candidates, and also the 'wandering stars' or planets under normal conditions. But with the planets there can also be abnormal situations – conjunctions, massings and occultations – and these must be taken very seriously indeed.

Of the five planets which are bright naked-eye objects we can at once eliminate Mercury, which is never prominent enough to be involved. This leaves us with Venus, Mars, Jupiter and Saturn. Of the remaining planets, Uranus is just visible without an optical aid if you know exactly where to look for it, but it shows up only in the guise of a very dim star, and the outermost members of the Sun's family – Neptune and Pluto – are much fainter, so that they could not possibly have been known in ancient times. Details of the bright planets are:

| Planet | Mean distance from Sun | | Orbital Period | Mean orbital velocity | | Maximum Magnitude |
	(10⁶ x miles)	(10⁶ x kms)		(miles/sec)	(kms/sec)	
Venus	67	108	224.7 days	22	35	- 4.4
Mars	142	230	687.0 days	15	24	- 2.8
Jupiter	483	777	11.9 years	8	13	- 2.7
Saturn	886	1426	29.5 years	6	10	- 0.3

Magnitude is a measure of apparent brilliancy. The scale works in the manner of a golfer's handicap, with the brightest performers having the lowest values. The Pole Star is of magnitude +2; Aldebaran, the red star in Taurus is +1; Sirius, the brightest star in the sky, is –1.5, and Canopus considerably fainter at –0.7. On the same scale, the magnitude of the full Moon is around –13, and that of the Sun is –27. The dimmest stars normally visible with the naked eye on a clear night are of magnitude +6, while modern electronic equipment, used with large telescopes, can reach down to +30.

Venus and Jupiter are always brilliant, and Saturn does not change by as much as a magnitude, but Mars does. At its best it can outmatch even Jupiter, as it will do briefly in August 2003, but at other times it is not a great deal brighter than the Pole Star.

According to the laws of planetary motion laid down by the German mathematician Johannes Kepler in the early seventeenth century, the orbital speed of a planet depends upon its distance from the Sun: the further out, the slower the speed. Thus the Earth moves at an average rate of 18 miles per second (29 kilometres per second), which is slower than Venus but quicker than Mars, Jupiter or Saturn, while the outer members of the Solar System are more leisurely still. The rates change slightly, because the orbits of the planets are somewhat elliptical rather than perfectly circular, and the velocities are greatest at the time of perihelion, the point of closest approach to the Sun. Bright comets, whose orbits are very eccentric, move very quickly when in the inner part of the Solar System, but when far away, beyond the orbits of all the main planets, they crawl.

There are times when two or more planets lie in much the same direction as seen from the Earth, and so appear side by side in the sky. When two planets are involved, we have what is termed a conjunction; if there are three or more planets taking part, the result is known as a planetary massing.

Very occasionally one planet may pass in front of another and hide or occult it. This last happened in January 1818, when Venus occulted Jupiter; the next occasion will be on 22 November 2065, which is rather a long time to wait. Ordinary conjunctions are more common, and with Jupiter and Saturn they occur every twenty years or so; for instance in May 1941, February 1962, March 1982 and May 2000.

Conjunctions between Venus and the two outer giants are less frequent, though on 21 July 1859 and again on 6 February 1892, Venus and Jupiter were very close. At the 1859 conjunction their centres were only 32 minutes of arc apart, so that to the naked-eye observer they were briefly merged. Remember, 32 minutes of arc is almost the same as the apparent diameter of the full Moon (30 minutes of arc is half a degree).

Venus and Jupiter were never at close conjunction during the period from 7 to 4 BC, and so we cannot look there for an answer to the Star of Bethlehem, but there are various other factors to be taken into account. One of these involves the phenomenon known as retrograding. In the usual way a planet moves against the starry background in a west-to-east direction, but near opposition there is a spell when the eastward drift stops, to be replaced by an east-to-west motion; then comes another stationary point, and the normal direction is resumed. In the diagram, I have shown the orbit

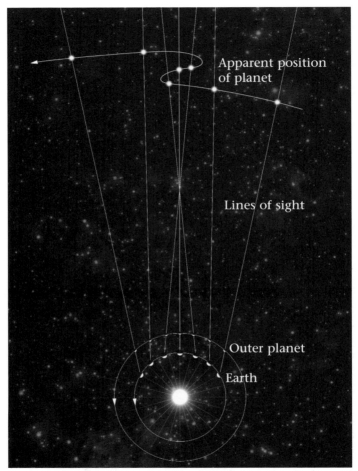

Retrograde motion of an outer planet. The orbits of the Earth and the planet are shown. When the Earth 'catches it up' and passes it, the planet appears to describe a long, slow loop in the sky.

of the Earth and also that of one of the outer planets (it does not matter which; the diagram is not to scale). As the Earth catches up the slower moving planet and passes it, the planet describes a slow loop in the sky.

It was this sort of behaviour which so puzzled the astronomers of ancient times, because retrograding is very hard to explain with the assumption that the Earth is the central body. Ptolemy was forced to introduce all sorts of complications (see page 25) so that in the end his system became hopelessly clumsy and artificial. Removing the Earth from its central position and putting the Sun there instead removed many of the worst problems, but not many of the Greeks could force themselves to consider anything so drastic.

It sometimes happens that Jupiter, Saturn and the Earth are so placed that there are three conjunctions one after the other. The last of these triple conjunctions was in 1940–41

Conjunction of Venus and Saturn, 7 BC; computer-aided reconstruction.

and in 1981; before 1940 there had been none since 1683. At the triple conjunction of 1981, in Virgo, the two planets passed close to each other on 14 January, 19 February and again on 30 July, but they never merged into a single naked-eye object, and they were very different in brightness; the magnitude of Jupiter was –1.7, that of Saturn only +1.1. Of course they were not genuinely close together; Jupiter was about 414,000,000 miles (666,000,000 kilometres) from the Earth and Saturn as much as 799,000,000 miles (1,286,000,000 kilometres), so that Saturn was very much in the background. The next triple conjunction of Jupiter and Saturn will occur in the year 2238.

I am not digressing, because there was a triple conjunction of Jupiter and Saturn in 7 BC, and this is one of the favourite explanations for the Star of Bethlehem. It is the choice of David Hughes, who has studied the evidence as carefully as anyone in the world. It is with the greatest diffidence that I take a contrary view, but everyone is entitled to have his own opinion, and in my view the triple conjunction theory has horribly weak links.

There had been a previous triple conjunction of Jupiter and Saturn in 146–145 BC, in Cancer. There are no surviving observations of it, but it must have been interesting to watch. The closest approach took place on 18 October 146 BC when the two were separated by 11 minutes of arc, which is around one-third the apparent diameter of the full Moon. The next approach, on 10 December, brought the two within 15 minutes of arc of each other; during the third, on 4 May BC 145, they were a mere 10 minutes of arc apart – nearly, though not quite, close enough for the two to fuse into one object from the viewpoint of the naked-eye observer.

During the triple conjunction of 7 BC, the only one which falls within our period, the two planets were in Pisces, the Fishes. On 27 May 7 BC, they were one degree from each other, so that they were well separated. Then they moved apart, to approach each other again during October; on the 6th of that month they were again one degree apart. Another separation, and a final approach on 7 December, again at a range of just over one degree. After that they moved apart relatively quickly.

It is evident that this triple conjunction was less spectacular than that of 145 BC, and in fact it was not spectacular at all. Jupiter is always brilliant, but Saturn was more or less at its faintest, with a magnitude of +0.5, slightly inferior to the star Procyon in Canis Minor (the Little Dog) and two whole magnitudes fainter than Sirius.

Saturn's opposition magnitude varies because of the changing tilt of the rings as seen from Earth. The rings are made up of millions of tiny pieces of ice, all swirling round the planet in the manner of dwarf moons, and are actually more reflective than the globe of Saturn itself. The rings measure 340,000 miles (600,000 kilometres) from tip to tip, but they are very thin, and their thickness must be less than a mile (less than 2 kilometres). When they are tilted edgewise on to us, as they were in 1995, they appear only as a thin line of light even in large telescopes, and with smaller instruments they vanish altogether for a brief period while the Earth and the Sun pass through the ring-plane.

(At the edgewise presentation of 1966, I was using the Lowell 24-inch refracting telescope at Flagstaff in Arizona (this was the time when I was very busy mapping the Moon). I could just about follow the rings through the whole period, but not at all easily.)

When the rings are best placed, as during the opening years of the present century, Saturn is much brighter and outshines all the stars apart from Sirius and Canopus. In 7 BC the ring tilt was 7 degrees, and Saturn was a long way off its maximum magnitude.

Changing aspects of Saturn's rings. Saturn is brightest when the rings are 'wide open' as seen from Earth (positions 3, 7). Illustration by James Symonds.

Matthew says nothing definite about the brightness of the star. True, the Protoevangelium of James does so: "an indescribably great star which dimmed the surrounding stars" – and I will come back to this later when discussing supernovae, but of course James' account was written long after Matthew's, and is at best no more than second-hand.

Quite apart from this, note that the minimum distance between Jupiter and Saturn was never much less than one degree. There was never any chance of their merging – and yet Matthew says quite definitely that the object was a star, not a pair of stars. So do the other accounts, vague though they are. It has been suggested that Matthew used the singular 'star' because the word 'planet' is not found anywhere in the Greek Old Testament, but this seems rather glib.

However, to my mind the worst objection of all is that apart from being singularly unspectacular, the whole sequence of events took over seven months. Herod himself could have seen it simply by looking up into a clear sky. The wise men would have known all about it and while they may have assigned a certain significance to the event, it is unlikely. Had Saturn been comparable in brightness with Jupiter, the triple conjunction theory would be slightly more plausible, but, as we have noted, Saturn merely looked like an ordinary star.

There was a conjunction of Jupiter and Saturn in the summer of 2000, and from the accompanying photograph you can see how wildly unequal the two are in appearance. It seems to me, therefore, that the triple conjunction idea fails all our requirements apart from 1 and 4.

It may be worth going back for a moment to meetings between Venus and Jupiter, because both these planets are so bright, and when close together they do make a brave showing – as they did, for example, on 23 February 1999, when they were only 8 minutes of arc apart. Way back on

Jupiter and Saturn, summer 2000; photograph by Christopher Doherty. Jupiter is the lower and brighter. The two stars to the right are Castor and Pollux in Gemini.

3 January 1818, Venus occulted Jupiter, and at that time the two planets were 16 degrees west of the Sun, so that the event ought to have been observable; but there is no record of it, probably because it was visible from only a very sparsely populated area of the Far East. The next occultation of Jupiter by Venus which will be seen at an elongation of more than 10 degrees from the Sun will be on 14 September 2123.

Looking back to the time of Christ, we find two very interesting events. On 12 August 3 BC, Jupiter and Venus were only 12 minutes of arc apart, in Leo, and would have been seen in the eastern sky before sunrise. Then, on 17 June 2 BC, there was an even more spectacular conjunction, again in Leo. At sunset on that day the planets would still be separate, appearing as a magnificent 'double star', but two hours later they would have merged into one, with a separation of only 3 seconds of arc, though by then they would have been on the verge of setting below the horizon.

The magnitude of Venus was −4 and that of Jupiter −2, but, rather surprisingly, when they fused together they would have produced an object no brighter than magnitude −4.2. As David Hughes has pointed out, it is wrong to suppose that a new, brilliant object would be seen, more brilliant by far than the two planets seen separately; the brighter planet (Venus) would simply seem to 'swallow up' the fainter one (Jupiter). In any case, the conjunction is too late. There is no reasonable doubt that by 2 BC, Christ was already a small boy.

A very different theory, again involving Jupiter, has been proposed by Michael Molnar, an American astronomer at Rutgers University in New Jersey. It came out in 1999, and caused a great deal of interest, possibly because it was so novel. According to Molnar, the Star of Bethlehem was due to two occultations of Jupiter by the Moon.

Planets, and some bright stars within the zodiacal band, can be occulted by the Moon. Antares, Aldebaran, Pollux, Spica and Regulus are all occulted from time to time, and these events are not particularly rare. Occultations of stars have always been regarded as important. When a star is occulted by the Moon, it shines steadily right up to the moment of occultation; when the Moon's limb sweeps over it, it snaps out as suddenly as a candle-flame in the wind. This is because the Moon has, to all intents and purposes, no atmosphere. If it had, then the star would flicker and fade before vanishing, because its light would be coming to us through the layer of atmosphere round the Moon's limb.

This does in fact happen when Venus occults a star, as it did on 7 July 1959, when the star concerned was Regulus in Leo. I observed the event with a 12-inch reflecting telescope, and the flickering and fading was very noticeable for several seconds before immersion, providing useful information

Occultation of Saturn by the Moon; photograph by Paul Doherty. Note how small Saturn appears compared to the Moon!

about the height and density of the atmosphere above the limb of the planet. Later, when data from spacecraft became available, it was found that the occultation results were remarkably close to the mark.

The occultation of a bright star is interesting to watch, particularly if immersion takes place at the Moon's sunlit limb, but in general you need binoculars or a telescope for a really good view, and it so happens that none of the dozen most brilliant stars can ever be occulted. Even Aldebaran is only marginally above magnitude +1.

Things are different with an occultation of a planet, because a planet shows a disk, and both immersion and emersion are gradual. A planet looks very small compared with the Moon, as the accompanying photograph shows, but all the same it takes an appreciable time to be covered.

Long ago one astronomer, W.H. Pickering, believed that when Jupiter was occulted, a band was seen across the disk of the planet which was attributed to a lunar atmosphere, but this is now known to be absolutely out of the question. The total weight of the entire lunar atmosphere is no more than about 30 tons (30,000 kilograms). If it were compressed to the density of the Earth's air at sea level, it would just about fill the Festival Hall in London, and it could not possibly have any observable effects upon light passing through it.

It so happens that there were four occultations of Jupiter in 6 BC, which is just within our acceptable time limits. Two of these (on 20 February and 15 May) took place when the Moon was below the horizon from the Middle East, and this leaves us with the occultations on 20 March and 17 April.

Michael Molnar was first drawn to the occultation theory when he examined two old coins, one issued in AD 13 or 14 and the other in AD 55. Both showed a ram looking at a bright star close to a crescent Moon. He concluded that these represented observations of the occultations of Jupiter in 6 BC, both of which occurred in the constellation of Aries, the Ram. This constellation was then the first constellation of the Zodiac because it contained the vernal equinox – that is to say, the point in the sky where the Sun crosses the equator around March 22 each year, moving from south to north. (The vernal equinox has now shifted into the adjacent constellation of Pisces, the Fishes.) Astrologically, Molnar considers that these occultations were indicative of some unusual event, such as the birth of the Messiah. Hence the journey of the wise men...

When I first heard about this theory I have to admit that I was immediately sceptical, mainly, though not entirely, because it is unlikely that the wise men would have seen either of the occultations of 6 BC. At the time of the 17 April occultation the Moon was above the horizon from Jerusalem

– not from Babylon – but the Moon was only one day before new. In addition, the occultation took place near noon, so that both Jupiter and the crescent Moon would have been drowned by the sky brightness, and the occultation could not possibly have been seen.

The prospects for the March occultation are only marginally better, but the occultation took place just after sunset when the Moon was already below the horizon of Babylon. From Jerusalem the altitude of the Moon was only 5 degrees, and the chances of the event being observed were practically nil. If there is any truth in the theory we have to assume that the Magi knew about, and interpreted, something they could not have seen, and, to put it mildly, this does not sound very probable.

There was a much more favourable occultation of Jupiter on 13 July 17 BC, and since it occurred about an hour and a half before sunrise it could well have been seen against a darkish background. But of course 17 BC is much too early to be of any help to us here, and all in all I fear that we must regard the occultation theory as both interesting and ingenious, but not correct.

Different again is the theory proposed in 1996 by J.N. Harris, who believed that the Star of Bethlehem was due to an accidental detection of the planet Uranus. This strikes me as being very peculiar, but for the sake of completeness it seems only fair to say a little about it.

Uranus was the first planet to be discovered in 'telescopic' times. It was found in March 1781 by William Herschel, who had come to England from his native Hanover, taken up astronomy as a hobby, and had made reflecting telescopes which were the best of their time. With one of these, a reflector with a mirror seven inches in diameter, he began a 'review of the heavens', with the aim of finding out how the stars in our Galaxy are arranged. Suddenly he came across an object which was most certainly not a star. It showed a disk and moved slowly from night to night against its background.

Herschel believed it to be a comet, but as soon as the orbit was worked out – initially by the Finnish astronomer Anders Lexell – it was found that the object was a planet, moving far beyond the orbit of Saturn, the outermost member of the Solar System known in ancient times. Its mean distance from the Sun is 1,783,000,000 miles (2,870,000,000 kilometres), and its revolution period is 84 years. After some discussion it was named Uranus, in honour of the first ruler of Olympus. It proved to be an icy gas giant, more than 30,000 miles (50,000 kilometres) in diameter.

Uranus can just be seen with the naked eye as a dim speck, provided that you know exactly where to look for it. In fact it had been recorded several times before 1781, but it had always been mistaken for an ordinary star, which is not at all surprising. Binoculars show it easily, and with a telescope it shows a pale, greenish disk. In 1986 it was passed by the spacecraft Voyager 2, and was found to be an unusual sort of planet; its axial inclination is more than a right angle, leading to a bizarre calendar, and the rotation period is just over 17 hours. There is a system of thin, dark rings, and there are around twenty satellites, all smaller than our Moon.

Uranus is a slow mover; during the Nativity period it lay in Pisces, and in 9 BC it was close to Saturn in the sky. According to Harris, the Magi detected it, realized that it was unusual, and tracked it during the subsequent years. This seems improbable in the highest degree, and even if the wise men had seen Uranus there is no way in which they could have realized that it was anything but a very inconspicuous star. This particular theory fails virtually all of our requirements.

However, we have not yet finished with the planets, and we must next turn to events which really are spectacular: planetary massings.

Three planets in the evening sky, with the crescent Moon; Saturn high up, Jupiter lower down, Mars to the right. Computer reconstruction, 6 April 2000.

Chapter 6
A MEETING OF PLANETS

Stargazers in Britain were very much on the alert on the evening of 6 April 2000. Half an hour after sunset there was a lovely grouping of planets. Saturn was fairly high in the south west, the much more brilliant Jupiter below it, and the fainter Mars just to the right of Jupiter. There, too, was the thin crescent Moon. This was a planetary massing – not a close one, but very beautiful. It lasted for a while before the planets and the Moon sank below the horizon.

I saw the spectacle from Selsey in Sussex, where I live. Later in the evening something else happened: a display of aurora borealis or Northern Lights, the best for ten years. This was sheer coincidence, because the aurora had absolutely nothing to do with the planetary massing, but it certainly added to the enchantment of the evening.

As we have noted, a grouping of three or more planets is officially called a massing, even when the grouping is not tight. On this occasion all the participants – the Moon and the three planets – were contained in a circle 5 degrees in diameter, and bearing in mind that the apparent diameter of the full Moon is about half a degree, this is not very much. The massing lasted for some time, until the planets disappeared into the evening twilight during May; at the end of the month they reappeared before dawn, but the main display was over.

This time, the two inner planets – Mercury and Venus – were not in the scenario, but this can happen, and indeed will happen on the evening of 8 September 2040, when all five naked-eye planets, plus the crescent Moon, will be grouped together. (I hope to see it, assuming of course that I live to the age of a hundred and seventeen.) This is not a digression, because there have been frequent suggestions that the Star of Bethlehem may have been due to a massing of planets.

The idea came originally to Johannes Kepler, the man who first showed that the planets move round the Sun in ellipses rather than in circles, and who laid down the three laws of planetary motion upon which all later work has been based. On 17 December 1603, Kepler saw a conjunction of Jupiter and Saturn, in Pisces, and began thinking about the star. During October 1604 Jupiter, Saturn and Mars were within 8 degrees of each other, on the borders of Scorpius and Sagittarius. However, Kepler himself later discarded the idea that the Star of Bethlehem might have been caused by a massing of planets. He believed that it was due to a bright new star, or nova, and this was natural enough, because in 1604 he observed what is now termed a supernova, a tremendous stellar outburst involving the death of a massive star.

I will have more to say about supernovae later. Meanwhile, let us deal with planetary massings, and see whether they can help us to solve our problem.

When the planets line up, as happens not too infrequently, astrologers and other eccentrics become very excited. All sorts of dire predictions are made, many forecasting the end of the world. It is claimed that the gravitational pull of the various planets, acting in the same direction, will cause tidal disturbances in the Earth and even in the Sun, with dramatic results.

The most notorious prediction of this kind was made as recently as 1982, and was sparked off by two science writers, John Gribbin and Stephen Plagemann. In March of that year there was a rough alignment of several planets, and according to Gribbin and Plagemann this would 'stretch out' the Sun; there would be great eruptions on the solar surface, and electrified particles shot out from the disturbed Sun would hit us, affecting the Earth's rate of rotation. This in turn would set up strains in the terrestrial globe, triggering off earthquakes. In particular, Gribbin and Plagemann referred to the San Francisco area, where a weak line in the Earth's crust known as the San Andreas fault has long been viewed with misgivings, and did actually produce a major quake in 1906.

However, the most elementary mathematical analysis is sufficient to show that even when all the planets are pulling in the same sense, the combined force is absolutely negligible. It has been calculated that the tidal stretching of the Sun could never amount to more than a few millimetres, which is not much when you remember that the Sun is 865,000 miles (1,400,000 kilometres) in diameter. Moreover we know that the Sun's surface pulses up and down in periods ranging from several minutes to several hours, which is more than enough to mask any planetary effects.

The 'Jupiter Effect' as Gribbin called it, was cleverly publicised, and caused real alarm. A programme at the London Planetarium, called 'Omens', frightened so many children that I eventually persuaded the planetarium authorities to take it off, though not until it had run for several weeks. The

Royal Greenwich Observatory was forced to put out an official statement, and even after I presented a special *Sky at Night* programme on BBC television the letters continued to pour in. It was at least a couple of months before the hue and cry died down, and it even spread to the United States.

I have mentioned this only to point out that planetary alignments and massings are quite harmless, and are due merely to line of sight effects, but even today we still have to reckon with the astrologers, who are always very vocal at such times. Even in 2000 they were at work, forecasting earthquakes, tidal waves, volcanic eruptions, wars, plagues and so on. At past massings there have been widespread panics.

In 1524 a well-known astrologer, Johann Stoffler, realized that during February, Mars, Jupiter and Saturn would all be in Pisces, the Fishes; Pisces is a watery sign, and so clearly a major flood was imminent. Stoffler's reputation ensured that he would be taken seriously, and as the critical time approached there was alarm over much of Europe; President Auriol of the University of Toulouse went so far as to build an ark to carry his nearest and dearest, though when nothing happened he explained, rather lamely, that he had wanted it only to go on a fishing trip.

There is no point in saying more here (see my book *Countdown*, Pan Books, London 1999), but it is worth mentioning that the closest grouping over the past few thousands of years was that of 26 February 1953 BC, when all the naked-eye planets were massed within a circle of only just over 4 degrees in diameter. An almost equally close massing occurred on 28 May 1059 BC. But what about planetary massings during the Nativity period?

There was one: in February 6 BC, when Mars, Jupiter and Saturn were within 8 degrees of each other. Again the constellation was Pisces, which was of importance to astrologers, but visually it was not at all spectacular. A year later, on 20 February 5 BC, the Moon passed close to Jupiter, and Mars and Saturn were close together some distance away. But the wise men would not have been particularly interested, and the phenomena fail requirements 2, 3, 5 and 6.

There was no hint of any unusual movement in the sky which would have led the Magi in the direction of Bethlehem; and as we have noted, St Matthew, who is really our only source of information, tells us that we are dealing with one star, not a group. This description simply does not fit in with any conjunctions or planetary massings. Try again!

Comet Arend–Roland, April 1957. This was a bright naked-eye comet. It will never return to our Solar System.

CHAPTER 7

Halley's Comet – and Others

In this investigation our main problem, all the way through, has been the lack of positive data. If St Matthew had not written those brief words about the star, nobody would ever have heard of it, and there would have been no controversy. On the other hand there must surely have been suggestions that Christ's birth must have been marked by some celestial display, and there are parallels; do you remember Owen Glendower's words as written by Shakespeare in *Henry IV Part I*? "at my nativity the front of heaven was full of fiery shapes; and at my birth the frame and huge foundation of the earth shaked like a coward. ... the heavens were all on fire, the earth did tremble."

But there may be very good reason why the Gospels give us so little to go on. In 1908 the famous astronomer E.W. Maunder wrote his book *The Astronomy of the Bible*, which has generally been regarded as the standard work on the subject, and he makes the following comment: "The purpose of the Bible is to reveal God to us, and to teach us of our relationship to Him. It was not intended to gratify the natural and laudable curiosity which has been the foundation of the physical sciences… There is no reason for surprise, then, that the information given to us concerning the Star is, astronomically, so imperfect."

This is reasonable enough, but one cannot help feeling irritated with St Matthew for being so unhelpful, though admittedly his purpose in writing may well have been different from ours. So where can we turn next in our search?

One suggestion seems to have been made first by Origenes Adamanthus, better known as Origen, who lived in Alexandria from about AD 185 to 254. Origen was one of the so-called Apologists whose mission was to persuade the Roman authorities that the Christians were not simply bands of heretics and troublemakers (remember that in Origen's time, Rome was still officially pagan; the first Christian emperor, Constantine the Great, did not become ruler until AD 307). Around the year AD 248 – we cannot be sure of the exact date – Origen referred to the Star of Bethlehem, and so far as we know was the first to make any attempt to give a scientific explanation for it.

Origen wrote: "We think that the star which appeared in the east was a new star and not like any of the ordinary ones, neither of those in the fixed sphere nor of those in the lower spheres, but it is to be classed with the comets which occasionally occur, or meteors, or bearded or jar-shaped stars, or any other such name by which the Greeks may like to describe their different forms."

So can the Star of Bethlehem have been a comet? After all, comets are the most erratic members of the Solar System, and they can become brilliant. They are also apt to take us by surprise, so that at first glance Origen's suggestion seems logical enough. Origen's use of the word 'meteor', by the way, does not mean a shooting star; to the Greeks a 'meteor' was anything high in the atmosphere, and the term could be extended to cover all manner of phenomena, ranging from clouds to lightning, rainbows and aurorae.

Comets are genuine members of the Sun's family, but are not solid and rocky, so they are totally unlike planets. A comet has been described as 'a dirty snowball', and is very flimsy and short-lived by cosmic standards. Their masses are negligible, at least by planetary standards, and I once commented that a comet is "the nearest approach to nothing that can still be anything". The only substantial part is the nucleus, made up of ices containing rocky fragments.

Few cometary nuclei are as much as twenty miles in diameter. The ices are of various kinds: frozen water, methane, ammonia and carbon dioxide, for example, but water ice is usually the dominant constituent. The dirty snowball theory was first proposed by F.L. Whipple in 1950, and has been proved to be correct, but this was not the generally-held view in ancient times; then it was believed that comets were phenomena of the upper air, though one Greek philosopher, Anaxagoras (c. 500 BC) thought that they might be due to clusters of faint stars.

It was only in 1577 that the Danish astronomer Tycho Brahe, the most skilful of all pre-telescopic observers, showed that comets must be much further away than the Moon. They were always regarded as unlucky, and might well spell doom for mankind or even the entire world. Recall Shakespeare's words in *Julius Caesar*: "When beggars die, there are no comets seen; the heavens themselves blaze forth the death of princes."

Comets move round the Sun, but most of them do so in very eccentric paths. There are plenty of comets which have revolution periods of a few years – only 3.3 years in the case of Encke's Comet – but all these are comparatively faint, and usually remain below naked-eye visibility. Really brilliant comets have paths which are much more elliptical, so that they cannot be predicted, and may have revolution periods of hundreds, thousands or even millions of years.

When a comet is far away in the outer reaches of the Solar System, it is simply an inert ice-ball. When it draws inward and is warmed, the ices begin to evaporate and a comet develops a head or coma; there may also be a tail or tails. Tails are of two types, some made up of dust and others of thin gas, but many bright comets have tails of both kinds. One interesting point is that the tails always point more or less away from the Sun. The gas tails are 'pushed out' by the slight but persistent force of the solar wind – a stream of particles being sent out by the Sun in all directions all the time – while the dust tails are repelled by the pressure of sunlight, which is sufficient to push outward the tiny dust particles which escape from the nucleus. When a comet is moving outward from the Sun, it travels tail-first.

The fact that the coma and the tails are produced by material expelled from the nucleus means that the comet must waste away. Eventually all its volatiles will be used up, and all that will be left will be the small, inert, icy nucleus. The short-period comets make regular returns to perihelion, and lose material each time; several comets which were known to have periods of a few years have now disappeared. The long-period comets return to perihelion far less frequently, so that they persist for much longer.

Comets are usually named after their discoverer or co-discoverers; thus the brilliant comet of 1997 was Hale–Bopp, because it was found independently by the American observers Alan Hale and Thomas Bopp. In some cases the name honours the mathematician who first

Typical comet; diagram showing the straight gas (ion) tail and the curved dust tail.

worked out the orbit. This applies to Encke's Comet, and also to Halley's.

Short-period comets come from a belt of material moving round the Sun beyond the orbit of Neptune, outermost of the main planets; it is named the Kuiper Belt, after the Dutch astronomer Gerard Kuiper, who first suggested its existence. On the other hand, the long-period comets seem to

Long-period comets from the Oort Cloud.

come from the Oort Cloud, named after another Dutch astronomer (Jan Oort), a spherical shell of icy objects at a distance of about one light-year from the Sun. Of course the Oort Cloud objects are too faint to be seen, but if one of them is perturbed for any reason it may start to plunge toward the Sun, so that eventually it invades the inner part of the Solar System and comes within our range.

One of several things may then happen to it. It may swing round the Sun and return to the Oort Cloud, not to be seen again for a very long time. It may be perturbed by the gravitational pull of one of the planets, usually Jupiter, and be expelled from the Solar System altogether; this was the fate of one famous comet, Arend–Roland, which was prominent for a few weeks in the spring of 1957. (I have fond memories of Comet Arend–Roland, because it was the subject of my very first *Sky at Night* programme on BBC television: I am sorry that I will never see it again!)

The comet may plunge into the Sun and be destroyed, as seems to happen quite often. It may hit a planet, as Comet Shoemaker–Levy did in 1994, when it impacted Jupiter and caused disturbances in the outer gas of the giant planet which persisted for months. Or it may be forced into a short-period orbit, so that it will make regular returns to perihelion and will waste steadily away.

The classic case of a comet death is that of Biela's Comet, whose path was originally computed by the Austrian amateur astronomer Wilhelm von Biela. (By profession he was an officer in the Austrian Army.) The comet was found to have a period of 6.7 years, and was seen regularly, but in 1846 it astonished astronomers by breaking in half. The twins came back on schedule in 1852, when they were more widely separated. They were missed in 1859, because they were badly placed in the sky, but they were confidently expected back in 1866. They did not appear; they had vanished as effectively as the hunter of the Snark, and have never been seen again. However, in 1872 a bright meteor shower was seen to come from the place where the comet ought to have been; no doubt we were seeing the funeral pyre of the luckless comet.

The only bright comet to return regularly is Halley's, named after Edmond Halley, the second British Astronomer Royal. Halley saw it in 1682, and found that it followed the same path as comets seen previously in 1607 and in 1531; he concluded that these three were one and the same, so that it returned every 76 years and would come back once more in 1758. By that time Halley was dead, but the comet was picked up on Christmas night in 1758 by the Saxon amateur Palitzsch, and returned to perihelion in 1759. Since then it has returned in 1835, 1910 and 1986; it is next due in 2061.

Looking back at the old records, mainly Chinese, we can trace observations of Halley's Comet as far back as 240 BC, and perhaps even earlier. Every return since then has been documented, and at times it has been brilliant – as in 837, when according to contemporary accounts it cast shadows, and developed a tail stretching right across the sky. It was seen in 1066, as William of Normandy was preparing to invade England, and was regarded by the Saxons as an evil omen; it is shown in the famous Bayeux Tapestry, with King Harold tottering on his throne and his courtiers looking on aghast.

Another return was that of 1301, when the comet was apparently seen by the Florentine painter Giotto di Bondone, who lived from 1267 to 1337. In about 1301 he was commissioned to paint a fresco for the Sorivegni Chapel in the Italian town of Padua, some way west of Venice. He obliged, and produced a beautiful fresco, 'The Adoration of the Magi'. There are the three kings, paying homage to the infant Christ – and there, in the sky, is a comet, probably Halley's, which the painter took to be the real Star of Bethlehem. Could he have been right?

Sadly, the answer must be 'no', because the comet returned to the perihelion in 12 BC, and this is well outside our limiting dates. Otherwise, it might well have been regarded as a promising candidate, and it is certainly worth casting around to see whether we can find any other comet which might meet our requirements.

We can reject all the short-period comets, very few of which ever reach naked-eye visibility; even when they do, they appear as nothing more than very dim, fuzzy patches. So we must see whether there are any records of really bright comets in the period from 7 to 4 BC.

Most records of old comets are Chinese. The objects are divided into three types:

1 Hui-hsing, or 'broom stars' – tailed comets which seem to sweep across the sky like brooms.

2 Po-hsing, or 'bushy stars', often described as 'sparkling'.

3 K'o-hsing, or 'guest stars', which appear stellar. Most are novae or supernovae, but a few could be cometary.

Obviously we cannot be confident that the Chinese records around the time of the Nativity are complete, but it does seem likely that any really bright comet would have been documented, because in general the Chinese were pleasingly meticulous. There are only two records between Halley's Comet of 12 BC (definitely too early) and a hui-hsing on AD 13 (equally definitely too late). But these two records are worth examining in detail.

The first comes from the astronomical chapter of the *Han shu*, a Chinese text dating back to around AD 130. It says that a hui-hsing was seen during March and April, 5 BC; it appeared in the area of Chhien-nu, and lasted for over 70 days. Chhien-nu is part of the Zodiac which we now include in the constellation of Capricornus, the Sea-goat, and includes the stars Alpha and Beta Capricorni. The object was on view between 10 March and 7 April in the morning sky; therefore it seems that the period of visibility was quite prolonged. Since it was seen from China, it must have also been seen from Jerusalem, and as it was described as a 'broom star' it can hardly have been anything other than a comet.

The other report dates from 4 BC, and again comes from the *Han shu*. It tells us that a po-hsing was seen in Ho-Ku, which is a region in Aquila centred on the bright star Altair;

How the comet of 5 BC may have appeared from Jerusalem.

Comet Hale–Bopp of 1996-97. This was a bright naked-eye
comet, though not brilliant enough to be visible in daylight.

also, a report from Korea confirms that a po-hsing appeared in April or May. The regions of Chhien-nu and Ho-Ku are only twenty degrees apart, and it is generally believed that the reports of 5 BC and 4 BC relate to the same object. The fact that the 5 BC object was described as a hui-hsing and the 4 BC object as a po-hsing is not significant, if only because the appearance of the object may have changed markedly during the 70 days when it was under observation, and of course it will have moved slowly but steadily against the starry background.

If we accept that there was only one object, and that it was seen during 5 BC, we must give it careful consideration. It was unusual, and it may have been conspicuous, though we do not know much about its brightness. It may have shifted eastward against the stars, and presumably it was widely observed. Yet remember that comets were always regarded as unlucky – so would the wise men have accepted one of these evil objects as a sign that the new Messiah had been born? It seems improbable.

There is a definite chance that the comet of 5 BC is associated with the Star of Bethlehem, and it is certainly the best candidate we have discussed so far, but there are still very serious objections. Requirements 3, 5 and 6 are not met, and our search is not over.

CHAPTER 8

EXPLODING STARS

The next suggestion – at first glance very promising indeed – is that the Star of Bethlehem was due to a colossal stellar explosion in which either a star suffered a violent outburst, flaring up temporarily to millions of times its normal brightness, or else a super-dense star literally blew itself to pieces. These are the novae and supernovae.

Our Sun is a steady, well-behaved star. It is shining not because it is burning in the manner of a coal fire, but because of nuclear reactions going on deep inside it. (A Sun made up entirely of coal, and burning as fiercely as the real Sun actually does, would turn to ashes in a few million years – but we know that the Earth is around four and half thousand million years old, and the Sun must be older than that.) Hydrogen is the Sun's fuel. It is the lightest of all the elements, and also the most plentiful in the universe, so that it is no surprise to find that the Sun contains a great deal of it.

The Sun is a huge globe, around 865,000 miles

(1,400,000 kilometres) in diameter, which is big enough to engulf well over a million globes the volume of the Earth. Deep inside it the temperature is very high, of the order of 15,000,000 degrees C. Under these extreme conditions of temperature and pressure, strange things are happening; the nuclei of hydrogen atoms are combining to build up nuclei of the second lightest element, helium. It takes four hydrogen nuclei to produce one helium nucleus, with the release of energy and loss of mass (or weight, if you like). It is this energy which keeps the Sun shining, and the loss in weight amounts to 600,000,000 tons (or tonnes) per second.

This may sound a great deal, but it is not much when you remember how vast the Sun is. Nothing dramatic is likely to happen to it for several thousands of millions of years in the future, but of course the supply of hydrogen is limited, and eventually the available 'fuel' will run low. The Sun must then change its structure. Different kinds of nuclear reactions will begin; the Sun's outer layers will blow out, while the interior will shrink and become very dense. The Sun will change into a red giant, as Aldebaran in Taurus and Arcturus in Boötes are now, and this must spell the end of the Earth, at least as a habitable world. Earth may be vaporized; even if not, it will become a seething, molten mass from which every vestige of life has been wiped out.

Next, the outer layers of the red giant Sun will be puffed off altogether, and for a brief period on the cosmic timescale the Sun will become a planetary nebula. (This is a bad term, because a planetary nebula is not truly a nebula and has absolutely nothing to do with a planet.) If you want to see one, take a telescope and look at a position near the brilliant blue Vega, which is almost overhead as seen from Britain during summer evenings. Close to Vega are two fainter stars, Beta and Gamma Lyrae; between them is the Ring Nebula, a very old star which has passed through its red giant stage and

The Ring Nebula, M57.

has now thrown away its outer layers. Over the centuries these outer layers will dissipate, and all that will be left will be a small, super-dense star of the type known as a white dwarf, still shining feebly but cooling down. Plenty of white dwarfs are known; Sirius, the brightest star in the sky, has a white dwarf companion, not much larger than the Earth but as massive as the Sun.

This is not quite the end of the story. After an immense period, all light and heat will leave the white dwarf Sun, and it will become a black dwarf – a stellar corpse, still circled by its remaining planets. It sounds rather depressing, but at least we on Earth are in no imminent danger, except of course from ourselves.

Our Sun is a single star, but there are many star-pairs, known as binary systems. In some cases the pair may consist of a normal star, often a relatively cool one, together with a white dwarf. The white dwarf pulls material away from its companion, and this material forms a ring or 'accretion disk' round the dwarf. Eventually the situation becomes unstable, and there is a nuclear outburst in the atmosphere of the white dwarf; gas is ejected at high velocity, and there is a tremendous, though temporary, increase in the output of energy. After the outburst, the system returns to its old state, and is none the worse. This phenomenon is termed a nova, and this again is a misleading term; nova means 'new', and a nova is not, in fact, a new star. It is an outburst in a very old star, far advanced in its evolution.

Novae can become very conspicuous. The star of 1918, which flared up in the constellation of Aquila (the Eagle), briefly outshone every star in the sky apart from Sirius, though it has now become an excessively faint telescopic object. An almost equally bright nova appeared in Perseus, in 1901. These two were exceptional, but naked-eye novae are not too uncommon, and there were ten between 1970 and 2000, though only one of these (Nova Cygni 1975) became as bright as the Pole Star. We must therefore look back at the records to see if we can find a nova to explain the Star of Bethlehem, but before doing so we must also consider even more violent explosions, known as supernovae.

Supernovae are of two distinct types. In Type I we begin with a binary system. The sequence of events is much the same as with an ordinary nova, but on a much larger scale, and the end result is different. The white dwarf builds up a gaseous layer from material stolen from its companion, but the body of the dwarf itself now consists largely of carbon. When the mass of the white dwarf exceeds a certain critical value, the carbon detonates, and the star literally blows itself to bits. At the peak of the outburst the luminosity may be as much as 4000 million times that of the Sun. In the end, the luckless white dwarf is no more.

Type II supernovae are different, because here we are not dealing with white dwarfs or binary systems. A very massive star – at least eight times as massive as the Sun – runs out of available nuclear fuel, admittedly only after a series of very complex reactions. There is an implosion, followed by an explosion, and the star is disrupted. Most of it is blown away into space, but the core of the old star is left, now made up of atomic particles called neutrons. A Type II supernova never reaches the luminosity attained by a Type I, but is still powerful enough to outshine the Sun by a factor of at least 1000 million.

The density of a neutron star is amazing; a thousand million tons of its material could be packed into a thimble, which would then weigh as much as an ocean liner. The neutron star is spinning round very quickly, and is sending out beams of radio radiation. When the Earth passes through one of these beams we receive a pulse of radiation, which is why some neutron stars are termed pulsars. Gradually they lose energy, and slow down, to end up as cold, inert globes, though in fact the universe as we know it may not yet be old enough for any of these dead stars to have developed.

Three supernovae have definitely been observed in our Galaxy over the past thousand years. That of 1006, seen in the southern constellation of Lupus (the Wolf) may have become as brilliant as the quarter-moon; it was poorly documented, but its remnant can still be traced by its radio emissions.

In 1054 a supernova blazed out in Taurus (the Bull) and remained visible with the naked eye in broad daylight for months. Its remnant is the Crab Nebula, a patch of expanding gas which is within the range of a small telescope, or even powerful binoculars. The nickname was given to it in 1845 by the third Earl of Rosse, when he first saw it through his curious but very effective homemade telescope at Birr Castle, in central Ireland.

The Crab Nebula is over 6000 light-years away, implying that the actual outburst took place in prehistoric times, but astronomers regard it as one of the most interesting objects in the sky. It contains a pulsar, flashing 30 times a second, and emits over the whole range of the electromagnetic spectrum, from the ultra-short gamma rays to the very long radio waves. A famous, though now somewhat hackneyed, comment by an eminent astronomer states that there are two kinds of astronomy: the astronomy of the Crab Nebula, and the astronomy of everything else!

There followed supernovae in 1572 (documented by the great Danish astronomer Tycho Brahe) and 1604 (observed by Johannes Kepler). Since then there has been only one naked-eye supernova, and this was not in our own Galaxy; it flared up during 1987 in the Large Magellanic Cloud, a satellite system of the Milky Way Galaxy at a range of 169,000 light-years. The supernova of 1987 has probably been studied more intensively than any other cosmic object

The Crab Nebula, M1.

in history, and has provided astronomers with a tremendous amount of information. It has not produced a pulsar, but one may well be detected in the future when the surrounding débris has had time to clear away. Even from its great distance, it still became almost as bright as the Pole Star.

We cannot tell when the next supernova will appear in our Galaxy. It may not be for centuries – but equally uncertainly, it might be tomorrow. So could the Star of Bethlehem have been a nova or a supernova?

Let us consider supernovae first. Certainly such an outburst would have been spectacular, and the wise men would have recognized it as being unusual, if only because they must have been very familiar with the star patterns. There is also a chance that the outburst might not have lasted for long. True, all the observed supernovae have remained brilliant for months, or at least weeks, but this is no positive proof that a supernova might not have faded much more quickly. A very interesting comment is made by E.W. Maunder in his classic book, *Astronomy of the Bible*. It runs as follows:

"I have somewhere come across a legend which may possibly afford the clue, but I have not been able to find that the legend rests on any authority. It is that the star had been lost in the daylight by the time that the wise men reached Jerusalem. It was therefore an evening star during their journey thither. But it is said that when they reached Bethlehem, apparently nearly at midday, one of them went to the well of the inn, in order to draw water. Looking down into the well, he saw the star, reflected from the surface of the water. This would of course be an intimation to them that the star was directly overhead, and its re-observation under such unusual circumstances, would be a sufficient assurance that they had reached the right spot."

Like Maunder, I have tried to trace the source of his legend. Like Maunder, I have failed, and I do not know where to look. But if the story is true, it shows two things. First, the star must have been not only brilliant, but outstandingly so, and this could only mean a supernova. Secondly, as Maunder points out, the star must have been exactly at the zenith or overhead point.

It is widely believed that from the bottom of a well it is easier to see the stars above, even during daylight, because of the darkness round you. In fact this is a myth. A few years ago I presented a television broadcast from the Homestake Mine in the Black Hills, South Dakota, not because of the Star of Bethlehem, but for a completely different purpose. (A special 'observatory' has been set up in the gold mine; it consists of a large tank of cleaning fluid, and has been trapping neutrinos sent out by the Sun.) From a depth of 4850 feet (1500 metres) below ground level I looked up at the sky. During night, the stars in the restricted field of view looked the same as they always do. When the sky was sunlit, no star could be seen because the contrast between the sky brightness and the brightness of the star was the same as it is from sea level.

The only way to check the Maunder story, or for that matter the whole supernova theory, is to examine the records and see if a supernova was seen around the time of the Nativity. Alas, we draw a blank. The records indicate that there was probably a supernova around AD 185, in the southern constellation of Centaurus, but there is nothing at all in the period before the birth of Christ. This may not be conclusive – as has been said time and time again, absence of proof is not proof of absence – but it would be very strange if there were no mention anywhere of a phenomenon as spectacular as a supernova would have been, and of course AD 185 is much too late to be considered. In any case, a supernova fails our requirements 3, 5, and 6.

Ordinary novae are much more common, as we have noted, and can become bright. If such a nova appeared during the Nativity period it could have matched any star, and could have been brief; the 1975 nova in Cygnus, which rose to magnitude 1.8, dropped below naked-eye visibility in less than a week.

Again we must look at the old records. The hui-hsing of 5 BC was a 'broom star' with a tail, which does not tie in with the possibility that it could have been a nova, and the po-hsing of the following year also seems to have been cometary, assuming that it may have been a separate object and not identical with the comet of 5 BC.

We cannot be sure, but it is worth noting that novae usually appear in or near the Milky Way region of the sky, and the object of 5 BC was in the barren constellation of Capricornus, which is some way from the galactic plane and is not the sort of place where one would expect to find a nova. However, there is some doubt about the precise position, and the Chinese and Korean records, which are the only ones available to us, do not agree. It has been suggested that the real site was not in Capricornus, but in Aquila, not far from the third-magnitude star Theta Aquilae.

Mark Kidger, who has undertaken a tremendous amount of research and for whose views I have the greatest respect, maintains that the 5 BC object really was a nova in Aquila. He goes on to link it with one particular star, listed in our modern catalogues as DO Aquilae. If he is right, then DO Aquilae is not an ordinary nova, but a star which has suffered more than one outburst.

Most novae flare up only once, but there are some which explode several times, and are called recurrent novae. The best-known case is that of T Coronae, in the little northern constellation of the Crown, not far from Arcturus. Normally it is around 10th magnitude, but in 1866 it rose abruptly to

DO Aquilae, some way from the brilliant Altair, as it might have been seen from Jerusalem in 5 BC. Now it is a faint variable star – but was it the Star of Bethlehem?

magnitude 2, so that it equalled Alphekka, the brightest star in Corona. It then faded back to its normal obscurity, but in 1946 it again rose temporarily to naked-eye visibility, so that it increased in brightness by a factor of 2000. If it flares up every 80 years or so, we may hope for another outburst around 2026, and no doubt astronomers will be keenly on watch. There are other known recurrent novae, and there is always a chance that DO Aquilae may come into this category.

Its usual magnitude is about 18, so that a telescope of fair size is needed to show it. (If you want to look, its position is RA

19h 31.5m, declination –6° 26′, between 42 and 26 Aquilae, south of Iota.) In 1925 it rose to magnitude 8.6, and was listed as a nova, but it soon faded conventionally back to its usual state. Since then it has done nothing unusual.

If DO Aquilae flared up in 5 BC, it would have been more or less in the right position, in the east at dawn, and it would not have remained bright for long, so that it does fulfil requirements 2, 4 and 5. For requirement 1 – that it was unusual – we must have grave reservations. The wise men could have noted a brilliant star in that position, but all the information we have leads us to suppose that DO Aquilae is not the sort of star to suffer an outburst major enough to make it a conspicuous naked-eye object. If it had behaved in this way, the after-effects would be traceable even now, probably at radio wavelengths, but nothing of the kind has been found. There is absolutely no chance that DO Aquilae was a supernova, and indeed no supernova remnant has been detected anywhere in the area.

No other novae have been documented in the period 7 to 4 BC, and of course no nova would move in the way in which, according to St Matthew, the Star of Bethlehem did, even considering diurnal motion (the motion due to the rotation of the Earth on its axis). Regretfully, DO Aquilae must be added to our list of rejects.

CHAPTER 9
HERE AND THERE

All our investigations up to now seem to have led us into blind alleys. What other possibilities are there? Let us do our best to exhaust these possibilities before making any attempt at an explanation and a summary.

We have cast out the familiar stars. Sirius was well known to the wise men and everyone else; Canopus, admittedly less familiar, fails most of our requirements, and no other ordinary stars are bright enough to be considered as candidates. There are, however, the variable stars. Most of these are predictable, but a few are not, and of these the most extreme is Eta Carinae in the southern sky.

Eta is indeed an extraordinary object. Over the past two centuries it has fluctuated wildly in brightness; at one period during the 1840s it surpassed even Canopus, and rivalled Sirius, so that for well over a decade it was glaringly conspicuous. It then faded, and for well over a hundred years now it has hovered on the brink of naked-eye visibility. It is a very massive, unstable star; at its peak it must have radiated as fiercely as six million Suns put together, and this has not declined much even now, though most of the radiation is at infra-red wavelengths.

The star is also associated with intricate nebulosity. When I first saw it through a telescope, I described it as an 'orange blob' quite unlike a normal star. It is 8000 light-years away, which is just as well from our point of view, because sooner or later it is bound to explode as a supernova, and indeed this may already have happened. Its final fate will be to produce a black hole. But as a Star of Bethlehem candidate, there is one factor which rules it out at once. Its declination is 60 degrees south, so that from Jerusalem it never rises above the horizon; it remains a degree or two below.

I have referred to Eta Carinae here because, although it is unique in our experience, there may be other objects of the same type which we have not identified because at present they are not bright enough. However, we come back to the same objections which we met in rejecting ordinary novae and supernovae.

One recent suggestion is due to Montague Richardson, who believes the star to have been Mira Ceti, a well-known variable with a mean period of 331 days. At its best it can become brighter than the second magnitude.

In 1597, a Dutch observer, David Fabricius, recorded a third-magnitude star in Cetus (the Whale). Subsequently he noted that it had disappeared, but apparently he thought no more about it. (Fabricius came to a sad end. He was a preacher, and during a sermon he hinted that he knew the identity of a parishioner who had stolen one of his geese. Before he could name the thief, he was murdered.)

Meanwhile his star was again seen at magnitude three in 1603 by Johann Bayer who was drawing up his famous catalogue and giving the stars the Greek letters which we still use. The letter 'omicron' was allotted to this particular star. Once again it vanished after a few weeks, and once again no attempt was made to follow it up. We are not sure whether Bayer knew about Fabricius' observation; probably he did not, or his suspicions would have been aroused.

Then, in 1638, another Dutchman, Phocylides Holwarda, was making observations of a total eclipse of the Moon when he saw the puzzling star again. Checking back in the records, he found that it had been previously seen not only by Fabricius and Bayer but also by a German astronomer, Wilhelm Schickard. He realized that it must be a variable, visible with the naked eye for only a short part of each year.

In 1648 Hevelius of Danzig, one of the leading observers of the time, named it Mira, 'the wonderful'. The name is still used, and indeed the numerous other variables of the same kind are known as Mira stars. All are well advanced in their evolution, and all are red.

Mira is a huge star, at least 400,000,000 miles (650,000,000 kilometres) in diameter, so that it could swallow up the whole orbit of Mars round the Sun. It is unstable; it swells and shrinks in a mean period of 331 days. The minimum magnitude is always about 9, but no two cycles are alike. At some maxima Mira never rises above the fourth magnitude, but now and then it becomes really prominent, as in 1987, when it matched the Pole Star. According to reports which are probably reliable, at the maximum of 1779, Mira became as bright as Aldebaran.

Richardson's suggestion is ingenious, but it fails too many of our requirements to be taken really seriously. It is wildly improbable that Mira could have become brilliant enough to attract general attention, and of course it would not move in relation to the nearby stars. There are no other Mira-type stars which can become bright enough to be

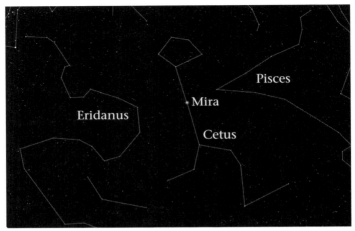

The position of Mira. A candidate star, but it is improbable that it became brilliant enough to attract general attention.

candidates, and from Jerusalem there is only one other (Chi Cygni, in the Swan) which can never reach the third magnitude.

It has been said that, according to Chaldaean astronomy, the constellation of Cassiopeia presided over Palestine, and this has led a researcher named Christopher McIntosh to suggest that it was this constellation which contained the Star of Bethlehem. Certainly it was here that Tycho's supernova of 1572 blazed forth, but this was a 'one-off'; a supernova destroys itself, and can explode only once.

The main stars of Cassiopeia are arranged in a rough 'W' or 'M' pattern, and are so far north of the celestial equator that over Britain they never set, though from Jerusalem they dip briefly below the horizon. They are not particularly bright, but the middle star of the W, Gamma Cassiopeiae – it has no individual name – is an interesting variable, quite unlike Mira. Usually it is of about the second magnitude, slightly fainter than the Pole Star, but it can show temporary outbursts, as it did in 1936, which raises it to a magnitude 1.6. It is an unstable star, and occasionally throws off shells of material which expand and cause a definite increase in brightness. But we have to say that Gamma Cassiopeiae is not a serious candidate, because it can never become brilliant enough and because it fails several of our other requirements.

There is also Betelgeux, the orange-red star in the upper left part of Orion (as seen from the northern hemisphere). Here we have a supergiant of immense size and 15,000 times as luminous as the Sun. It is variable, but unlike Mira it has no well-marked period; the usual magnitude range is between 0.2 and 0.9, and the variations are slow. There is a very rough cycle of between 5 and 6 years; but it *is* rough.

It is interesting to compare Betelgeux with Procyon in

Tycho's supernova as it might have appeared in 1572.

Orion; photograph by Christopher Doherty. Betelgeux is to the upper left of the constellation. Rigel, to the lower right. The Great Nebula lies below the three stars of the belt.

the Little Dog (magnitude 0.4) and Aldebaran in Taurus (0.9). Betelgeux has been known to match Rigel, the leader of Orion (magnitude 0.1), but this does not happen often. Even if there had been an exceptional maximum at the time of the Nativity, it cannot have been bright enough to catch the attention of the wise men, quite apart from the fact that as a candidate, Betelgeux fails most of our other requirements. It is the closest of the known red supergiants (*the Cambridge catalogue* gives its distance as 310 light-years, though this may be something of an underestimate). If it explodes as a supernova, as it certainly will do so one day, it will shine as brightly as the quarter-moon.

According to a completely different theory, the Star of Bethlehem may have been due to an exceptional display of aurora. This seems to fail virtually all our requirements, but since it has been suggested now and then I feel that I must dispose of it here.

Aurorae, or polar lights – Aurora Borealis in the northern hemisphere, Aurora Australis in the southern – are due to electrified particles sent out by the Sun. These particles cross the 93,000,000 mile (150,000,000 kilometre) gap between the Sun and the Earth, and reach the boundary of the terrestrial magnetosphere, the region inside which the Earth's magnetic field is dominant. This boundary acts in the manner of a barrier, and many of the particles are forced round the Earth's globe, following the magnetic field lines. The magnetic field is compressed on the 'day' side, and on the 'night' side of the Earth a magnetic tail is produced, stretching out for as much as 4,000,000 miles (6,500,000 kilometres). Some of the particles stream down into the upper atmosphere and make it glow rather in the manner of a spark coil. The result is an aurora. (I admit that this is a very over-simplified explanation, but the basic idea is clear enough.)

Because the particles are electrically charged, they tend to stream down toward the magnetic poles, and there are well-defined 'auroral belts' centred on each pole, so that aurorae are commonest at high latitudes. On average, displays can be seen on 240 nights per year in north Alaska, north Canada, north Norway and Iceland; 25 nights per year along the Canada–United States border and in central Scotland, and only one night per year in central France. From southern England there are occasional bright aurorae, as on 13 March 1989, 8–9 November 1991 and 6 April 2000, when the entire sky was coloured and there were arcs, ribbons and flaming surges. Conditions are the same in the Antarctic, but of course southern aurorae are much less widely observed because of the lack of population; most of the brilliant Southern Light displays are enjoyed only by penguins.

Aurorae are almost unknown in latitudes such as that of Jerusalem, but not quite. In 1909 there was a display which was seen even from Singapore, less than two degrees from the equator. Yet there is no possible way in which an aurora could be likened to a star, and this, in view also of the inherent impossibility of a major display taking place at the time of the Nativity, is sufficient to rule the whole idea completely out of court.

There is also the glow of the zodiacal light, which is cone-shaped, and is seen either above the western horizon after sunset or above the eastern horizon before dawn. Unlike the aurora, it is well outside the Earth's atmosphere, and is due to small particles moving round the Sun in the same plane as the Earth's orbit; they are lit up by the Sun, and the effect can be very beautiful. The zodiacal light is often seen from low latitudes (it has been nicknamed the 'false dawn'), but the wise men would have been very familiar with it, and would not have regarded it as in any way unusual.

The Polish astronomer Michael Kamienski, at the

University of Krakow, has suggested that the Star of Bethlehem may have been due to ball lightning. It is true that ball lightning is a rare and still somewhat mysterious phenomenon; it takes the form of a glowing sphere, varying in size from the size of a golf ball to a balloon several feet across, drifting slowly and erratically around. It may explode violently, and is quite definitely dangerous, but it lasts for only a short time – never more than a few minutes – and is so obviously low down that it could not possibly be mistaken for a star even if it met any of our other requirements.

Planets, conjunctions, occultations, comets, ordinary stars, variable stars, novae, supernovae, aurorae, the zodiacal light, ball lightning – what have we left? This is where I come to my own pet theory, which I know has weak points but which seems to me to be rather better than the others. I suggest that the Star of Bethlehem may have been due to two meteors.

CHAPTER 10
SHOOTING STARS

Meteors are the junior members of the Sun's family. They are nothing more or less than cometary débris, and most of them are smaller than grains of sand. Unless they dash into the upper air they cannot be seen, but if they enter the atmosphere, moving at anything up to 45 miles (72 kilometres) per second, they rub against the air particles and set up so much heat by friction that they burn away, ending their groundward journey in the form of fine dust. They burn out at an average height of 50 miles (80 kilometres) above sea level, producing the familiar shooting-star trails. What we see, of course, is not the tiny particle itself, but the luminous effects produced in the air during its suicidal plunge.

As a comet moves along, it leaves a dusty trail behind it. When the Earth passes through such a trail, we collect a great number of meteors, and the result is a shower of shooting stars. Because the meteors are travelling through space in parallel paths, the meteors of a shower seem to issue from one particular point in the sky, known as the radiant. The radiant is named after the constellation in which it lies; the Leonids from Leo (the Lion), the Lyrids from Lyra (the Lyre), and Taurids from Taurus (the Bull) and so on. The only exception to this refers to the Quadrantid shower of early January. This radiant lies in the old constellation of Quadrans, the Quadrant, which has been deleted from modern maps and absorbed into Boötes (the Herdsman).

There is a good way to show why the meteors seem to diverge from a radiant. Stand on a bridge overlooking a motorway, and you will see that the parallel lanes of the motorway seem to meet at a distant point.

Not all meteors are members of showers. There are also many sporadic meteors, which may appear from any direction at any moment and are not associated with known comets, though no doubt they have a cometary origin. Note also that there is no connection between shooting-star meteors and meteorites, which are much larger and may land intact, even producing craters. Meteorites mainly come from the asteroid belt; most museums have collections of them.

There are many annual meteor showers. Among the most important are the Quadrantids (1–6 January), the Lyrids (19–25 April), the Perseids (25 July–20 August), the Draconids (7–10 October), the Taurids (20 October–30 November), the Leonids (15–20 November), the Geminids (7–15 December) and the Ursids (19–25 December). The richness of a shower is given by its Zenithal Hourly Rate, or ZHR which is the number of naked-eye meteors per hour which would be expected to be seen by an observer under ideal conditions, with the radiant at the zenith. In practice these conditions are never fulfilled, so that the observed hourly rate is always rather lower than the theoretical ZHR. The ZHR values range from below 5 for weak showers, up to

Leonid meteors, 17 November 1966; photograph by Paul
Doherty.

more than 70 for the Perseids and the Geminids, but not all showers are consistent. The Perseids can always be relied upon, and anyone who stares up for a few minutes into a clear, dark sky during the first fortnight in August will be very unlucky not to see a meteor or two; the particles from the associated comet (Swift–Tuttle) have had time to spread all round the comet's orbit.

Other showers are erratic. The Leonids can produce 'meteor storms', as in 1833, 1866, 1966 and 2000, with a brief ZHR of many thousands; it has been said that on occasion meteors seemed to rain down like snowflakes for an hour or two. In other years the Leonids are sparse, because the shower is cosmically young and the meteors have not yet spread all round the orbit; as with the Perseids. We have to wait for the moment when the Earth plunges through the thickest part of the storm, as happens when the parent comet, Tempel–Tuttle, is close. The period of the comet is 33 years, which is why there were major displays in 1966 and 1999–2000. Some expected displays (1899 and 1933 for example) have failed to materialize, but the Leonid prospects for 2033 seem to be good.

It seems most unlikely that the Star of Bethlehem can have been due to a meteor shower. On the other hand, what about an isolated meteor or meteors?

Suppose that the wise men saw a brilliant meteor, rising in the east and crossing the sky in a westward direction, lasting for only a few seconds but leaving a visible trail persisting for hours. It could well have been spectacular; now and then we see a meteor which is brighter than the full moon, and one or two have been known to rival the Sun. Of course this on its own is not an adequate answer to the Star of Bethlehem, but let us take matters further. Later – how much later is irrelevant – a second brilliant meteor appears in the same place, and crosses the sky in the same way before

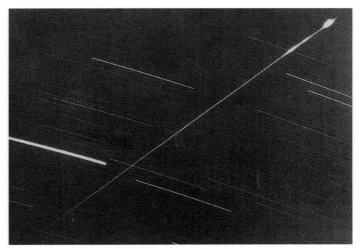

Exploding Perseid meteor, leaving a long trail.

vanishing. This would certainly be taken as a sign that something unusual was about to happen in the direction indicated.

The chances of two bright meteors following almost the same path are quite good, and there have also been more unusual phenomena – meteor processions, of which the best example was that of 9 February 1913. A procession was seen from parts of the New World, ranging from Toronto in Canada through to the Brazilian coast. Because it occurred on St Cyril's day, it is remembered as the Cyrillids.

According to a well-known astronomical historian, C.A. Chant of Toronto University: "At about 9.05 in the evening there suddenly appeared in the north-western sky a fiery red body. It moved forward on a perfectly horizontal path with a peculiar, majestic, dignified deliberation.

"Before the astonishment aroused by this first meteor had subsided, other bodies were seen coming from the north-west, emerging from precisely the same point as the first one. Onward they moved at the same deliberate pace, in twos or threes or fours, with tails streaming behind. They all traversed the same path, and were headed for the same point in the south-eastern sky."

The Cyrillids were seen by many people (including Chant), but they were of course totally unexpected, and there are no really precise measurements of them; we rely only on naked-eye estimates. Nothing like the Cyrillid procession has been seen since, but if a phenomenon of this sort happened once it may have happened quite often in the past. And if the wise men saw either a Cyrillid-like stream, or two particularly startling meteors moving in the same path, we could here have an explanation for the Star of Bethlehem which will satisfy at least some of our requirements.

First, it must have been unusual.

Secondly, it would have been very conspicuous.

Thirdly, it could have been seen only by the wise men, not elsewhere.

Fourthly, the date could well be right.

Fifthly, the phenomenon was brief.

Finally, the objects moved in a way quite unlike the behaviour of any ordinary body. None of our other suggested cosmic candidates could have done so.

Of course the main problem is, that if we accept St

Matthew's account, the star led the wise men to Bethlehem and then hovered over the place where Christ lay. This would certainly be very unmeteoritic behaviour, and we will have to allow Matthew a sufficient degree of poetic licence.

There is absolutely no way in which we could ever prove that two brilliant meteors, or a Cyrillid-like procession, appeared at the time of the Nativity. On the other hand, neither can we disprove it, and this theory does seem to be the only one to meet most of our requirements apart from the last.

My case rests.

CHAPTER **11**

THE ANSWER?

I have done my best to summarize the various theories about the Star of Bethlehem. Now let us take stock and see if we can give any really definitive answer.

I am assuming that St Matthew's account is the only one to carry any real weight, and that it is the one upon which all others are based. I am also assuming that Christ was born either in 4 BC, 5 BC or slightly earlier, as virtually all Biblical scholars agree; the idea that he was born as late as 1 BC seems very improbable, though even if so, the summary I give here is not really seriously affected.

It is always possible, of course, that more than one phenomenon is involved, and this is the belief of Mark Kidger, whose book ranks with David Hughes' as the best ever produced on the subject. According to Kidger, the signs in the sky which induced the wise men to go to Bethlehem were: (1) the triple conjunction of Jupiter and Saturn in 7 BC, (2) the massing of planets in 6 BC, (3) the planetary pairings in Pisces in 5 BC, and (4) the nova, later in 5 BC. However, these events are, to my mind, too spread out, and taken together they fail the all-important requirements 3, 5 and 6. In any case, as we have seen, there is serious doubt about the nature of the object seen in 5 BC. Finally, Matthew says quite definitely that he is referring to one 'star', although this was not an unusual generic term for a dark sky object.

Refer back, please, to the list of requirements given on pages 34–35. If we can find an object which fits all six of them, we may think that our search is over; but, alas, I fear that we will have to make do with some sort of compromise, unsatisfactory though this may seem.

The star was supernatural:

I feel that I can add very little to what I said in chapter 2. There are many people who believe the star to have been divine, and this is purely a matter of opinion. If it were indeed a message from God, then it is beyond science.

The star was Venus, Jupiter or any other planet or star 'on its own':

Fails requirements 1, 3, 5 and 6. The wise men certainly knew about all the familiar objects in the sky; remember, by their time there were very accurate star catalogues and planetary tables. There is every reason to assume that the wise men were well-informed. They may not have been very familiar with Canopus, which barely rises from Jerusalem, but Canopus fails requirements 1, 3, 5 and 6.

The star was due to the triple conjunction of Jupiter and Saturn in 7 BC:

Fails requirements 3, 5, 6 and probably 2. Saturn is never strikingly prominent, and in 7 BC the two planets were never close enough to merge into a single naked-eye object.

The conjunction was a prolonged affair, and if Herod had wanted to see it he need have done no more than go out and look. Moreover, though the triple conjunction was unusual, it does not tie in at all well with Matthew's description.

The star was due to a conjunction of the two most brilliant planets, Venus and Jupiter:
Ruled out by requirement 4. The only two Venus/Jupiter conjunctions anywhere near the time of the Nativity were too early. Requirements 3 and 5 are also not met.

The star was an accidental discovery of the planet Uranus:
Fails all our requirements, except just possibly 1. But since Uranus is barely visible with the naked eye it does not seem that this idea can be taken at all seriously.

The star was due to occultations of Jupiter by the Moon:
Fails requirements 3, 5 and 6, and probably also 2 because, as seen with the naked eye, an occultation, even of a planet as bright as Jupiter, is not at all eye-catching.

The star was due to the massing of planets in 6 BC:
Fails requirements 2, 3, 5 and 6. This again was a long drawn-out phenomenon, visible to anybody, and of course the movements of the planets do not tie in with Matthew's account, although some argue that it is the interpretation of such an event that may be important rather than the actual visibility.

The star was a comet:
Halley's Comet can be rejected at once, because it returned to perihelion years too early. The only other cometary candidate is the object of 5 BC, but this fails

requirements 3, 5, and 6, and very possibly 2 also. The Chinese describe it as a 'broom star', so that it was almost certainly a comet and not a nova. The object of 4 BC is probably identical with it.

The star was a nova or supernova:
The supernova theory can be ruled out at once because it is beyond belief that a strikingly brilliant outburst of this kind would have been ignored by everyone except the wise men. In any case, the supernova fails requirements 2, 3, 6 and possibly 5. The nova theory fails requirements 3, 6 and possibly 5.

The star was due to some other celestial phenomenon:
No variable star seems to meet any of the requirements except 1 and just possibly 2. Aurorae and zodiacal light fail all the requirements except 2 and 5. Ball lightning or any other low-level atmospheric phenomena are ruled out as being quite incompatible with the description given by St Matthew or any other writer.

The star was due to meteors – either two meteors appearing at different times and following similar paths, or else a Cyrillid-type meteor procession:
Fails requirement 6 and of course does not fit in well with Matthew's description. Yet meteors are the only natural objects which show definite movement across the sky over a short period of observation.

We must always bear in mind the purely astrological significance of the star, and we must accept that the wise men were astrologers first and foremost. And if the star really existed, its astrological implications must have been profound.

In the end, I fear that we have no definite answer. Whether we will ever solve the problem is highly unlikely. The chances of finding any more contemporary accounts are in effect zero, and all we can do is to interpret the little information available to us. It is not much, but it is better than nothing, and for this at least we must be grateful to St Matthew. All in all, there can be no doubt that the Star of Bethlehem will be remembered for as long as mankind survives on Earth.

APPENDIX

St Matthew's Account

From the new revised standard version of the Bible. Chapter 2, Verses 1–12 and verse 16.

"In the time of King Herod, after Jesus was born in Bethlehem of Judea, wise men from the East came to Jerusalem, asking, Where is the child who has been born King of the Jews? For we observed his star at its rising, and have come to pay him homage.

"When King Herod heard this, he was frightened, and all Jerusalem with him; and calling together all the chief priests and scribes of the people, he inquired of them where the Messiah was to be born.

"They told him, In Bethlehem of Judea, for so it has been written by the prophet: 'And you Bethlehem, in the land of

Judah, are by no means least among the rulers of Judah; for from you shall come a ruler who is to shepherd my people Israel.'

"Then Herod secretly called for the wise men and learned from them the exact time when the star had appeared.

"Then he sent them to Bethlehem, saying, Go and search diligently for the child, and when you have found him, bring me word that I may also go and pay him homage.

"When they had heard the King, they set out, and there, ahead of them, went the star that they had seen at its rising, until it stopped over the place where the child was.

"When they saw that the star had stopped, they were overwhelmed with joy. On entering the house, they saw the child with Mary his mother, and they knelt down and paid him homage. Then, opening their treasure-chests, they offered him gifts of gold, frankincense and myrrh.

"And having been warned in a dream not to return to Herod, they left for their own country by another road." [...]

"When Herod saw that he had been tricked by the wise men, he was infuriated, and he sent and killed all the children in and around Bethlehem who were two years old or under, according to the time that he had learned from the wise men."

Bibliography

HUGHES, DAVID.
The Star of Bethlehem Mystery
J.M. Dent, London 1979.

KIDGER, MARK.
The Star of Bethlehem:
An Astronomer's View
Princeton University Press, 1999.

MAUNDER, E.W.
The Astronomy of the Bible
T. Sealey Clark and Co,
London 1908.

MOLNAR, MICHAEL E.
The Star of Bethlehem:
the Legacy of the Magi
Rutgers University Press, 2000.

Index